Beyond Terminal

How One Belief Kept This Revivor Alive and Laughing!

Chris Collins

This is a work of nonfiction. Minor discrepancies are inevitable. Every detail cannot be guaranteed, but this book is as accurate as possible given the circumstances. The author acknowledges the trademarked status and trademark owners of various products referenced, which have been used without permission. The publication/use of these trademarks is not authorized, associated with, or sponsored by the trademark owners.

Because of legal necessities, I must state that this book is not meant to diagnose or suggest treatment for any illness. You must choose the correct practitioner for your needs. I am not a practitioner, and I do not suggest you turn away from yours. I have known many who have done well with the Western medical solutions, and I have leaned on them in years past for infections and accidents, among other things. I bless them all for their work.

ISBN-13: 978-0-9700703-3-3

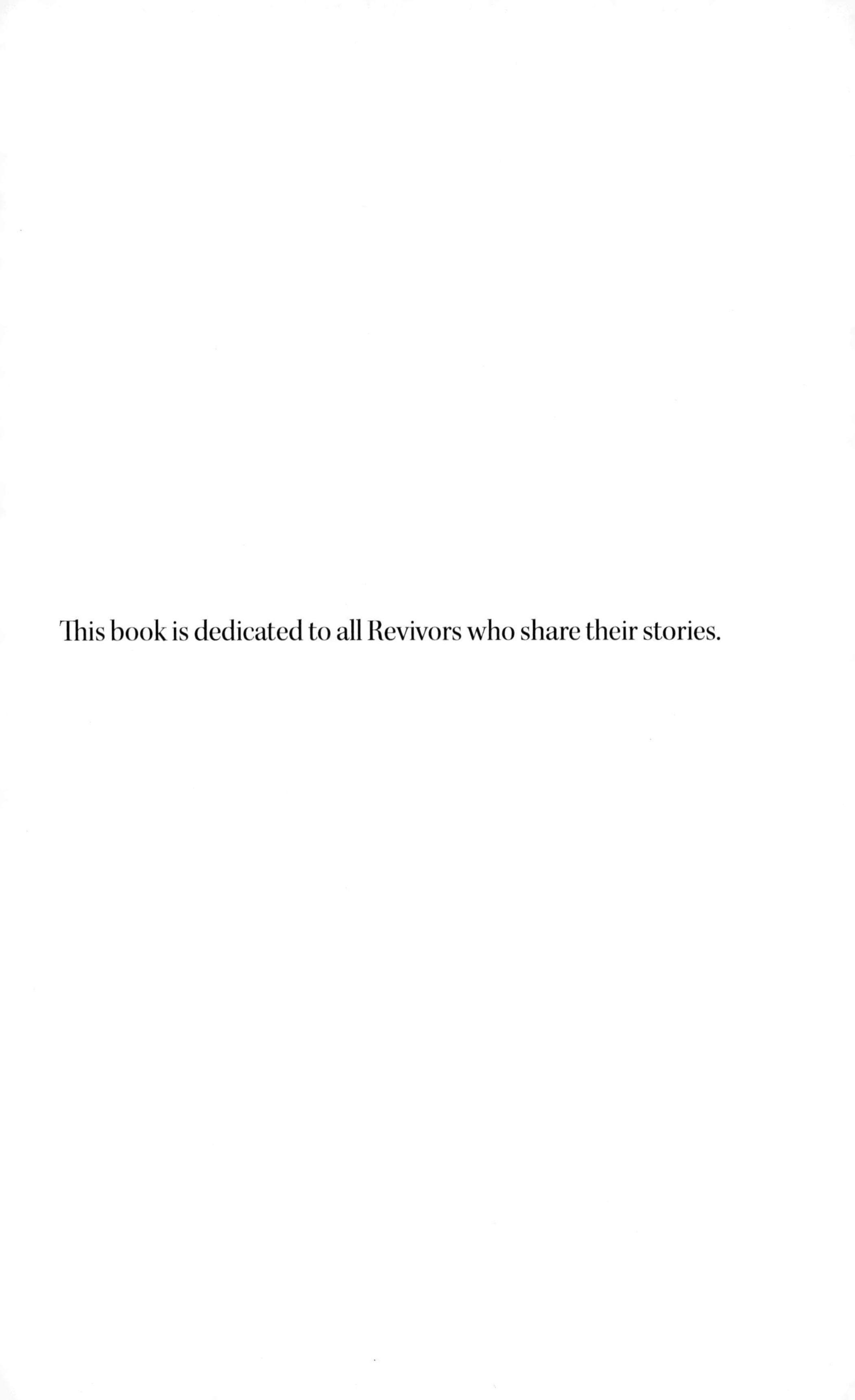

This book is dedicated to all Revivors who share their stories.

Table of Contents

AUTHOR'S NOTE

"It had been my repeated experience that when you said to Life, calmly and firmly, (but very firmly!), 'I trust you; do what you must,' Life had an uncanny way of responding to your need." – Olga Ilyin

Trust life? How could I possibly do that?

The doctor said three to six months, effectively extinguishing decades of my life in mere seconds. The very idea of trust was laughable—in fact I felt completely betrayed—and I suffered an uncontrollable desire to lunge forward and strangle the good doctor with his stethoscope. In reality, I hardly moved; I was lost, in chaos, and barely able to breathe.

This book was built on the premise that some people may need information about how others have healed themselves from a terminal diagnosis. I also wanted a "name" that was different from Survivor or Thriver for a reason. We are different.

Every day people are revived from the edge of death from drowning, heart attacks, stroke or other mishaps. It takes every bit of the body, mind and spirit to revive someone. After only three minutes, it becomes exhausting. We call these people heroes because it is an immense job that takes every bit of energy they have, and it works.

When we are trying to revive ourselves, it's the same thing. The body needs extreme help, the mind needs to stay calm and the spirit is called upon to do the impossible, stay alive. But this type of reviving takes more than sheer moments, it sometimes takes years. If you have a partner to help, that's wonderful. But truly, all responsibility lies with one person, the Revivor.

The Revivor knows that if healing happens, it will be because we used our own intuition and choices, most often using natural therapies, and we are grateful for whatever evolves.

In writing this book, I also felt it was okay to laugh, as I moved through an experience that everyone assumes is the end of the world. Often, it is not.

Some people might *not* be dying when they are given a terminal diagnosis. The simple truth is this: it often takes years for one cancer cell to grow into something that can be seen and/or felt. When a terminal patient is first diagnosed, he or she often has time to "fix" it with food, juice, an extreme change in lifestyle, a more personal knowledge of oneself. Plenty of folk are doing it. Just ask Chris Wark (colon cancer), Ann Cooper (pancreatic cancer), Lauren Ewing (ovarian cancer), Ed Moore (liver cancer), Terry Wahl (multiple sclerosis), Joyce Brown PhD (ALS), Karen Hale (Lupus) or any of the others on the Stories page of my website. If there are forty listed on my site alone, how many more have healed, but haven't written about it? I have no idea how many of you are out there, but I am positive there are at least one thousand times those forty. Our parents and grandparents have been using different options to heal, and "back in the day" many physicians were quick to say that the patient is the healer.

> "One of the first duties of the physician is to educate the masses not to take medicine." – Sir William Osler, 1st Baronet, Canadian physician and one of four founding professors of Johns Hopkins Hospital.
>
> "One must not forget that recovery is brought about not by the physician, but by the sick man himself. He heals himself, by his own power, exactly as he walks by means of his own power, or eats, or thinks, breathes or sleeps." – Georg Groddeck, physician and writer regarded as a pioneer of psychosomatic medicine.

"The aim of medicine is to prevent disease and prolong life, the ideal of medicine is to eliminate the need of a physician." – William J. Mayo, physician and surgeon in the United States and one of the seven founders of the Mayo Clinic.

"Much of your pain is the bitter potion by which the physician within you heals your sick self." – Khalil Gibran, third best-selling poet of all time, behind Shakespeare and Laozi.

It's hard for others to believe that we are actually healing from a terminal diagnosis. They want to see proof, see the numbers, know what the "doctor" says. Fortunately, the proof is within us, and sometimes outside of us.

When I began writing Beyond Terminal almost everyone I knew was familiar with someone who had, in some fashion, walked away from a terminal diagnosis, with cancer, ALS, MS, Lupus, among others, and most because of natural therapies. My diagnosis was a rare blood disorder, Aplastic Anemia. At that time, no one was writing about naturally healing blood related disorders, so I turned toward the largest population that was writing about it...cancer folk. My eyes were opened and I was amazed at what I found. And I wasn't the only one.

Kelly A. Turner, a PhD, and angel from my standpoint, thought it was strange that no one had researched the thousand plus cases in medical journals describing those who had used alternative means to healing. Their cancer was gone but no one had taken the time to find out why. She took on that challenge. At her website www.drkellyturner.com you can find examples of thousands who are using alternatives to traditional medicine. You can also include your own story. Dr. Turner's website is the best source I know of to find cancer Revivors. It's also the best "report" on what people are doing around the world in the fight against cancer.

We are indeed healing in different ways and I believe the very tip of the iceberg is in our line of sight. What about those we know nothing about, those who are healing but not reporting their process. My heart sings with the thought of all those people getting better.

What about *your* story?

You may discover new concepts and words in this book, but there is one you will not happen upon very often. If I ever say it, you have permission to smack me with a ruler!

I do not like, nor do I believe in the word *denial* regarding a diagnosis. I believe it is extremely hurtful, and devalues the folk who are going through these difficult times. They are not in denial, they are not dying. It's our Western medical machine that eventually sells them on the idea of a probable death, as I was almost "sold" after three months of thrice weekly blood and platelet transfusions.

There comes a point when people just give up, and accept what has been repeated over and over to them. Fatigue and malnutrition come into play and by that time, the die is cast.

Most buy it, but I didn't. Because you are reading this book, you have already decided what you will and won't buy.

I have had many of my relatives move to the "other side" because of cancer or other chronic maladies. No one wants to believe that their loved one passed simply because they bought the idea that they were, indeed, terminal. I don't think that's the case every time; however, I do think that our belief systems comprise over 50% of any healing that goes on.

Twenty years ago it was more common to accept a terminal diagnosis, and the Western medical treatment offered to combat it. If efforts were unsuccessful, *c'est la vie*. However, with the gift of the Internet came new opportunities to find alternative solutions.

Many Revivors have found their way to health simply because they had a sneaking suspicion that:

a) the diagnosis was "wrong" or that

b) their physician did not understand who they were diagnosing, or

c) it was not time to give up even though their physician already had by telling them there was nothing to be done.

These folk took a turn for the better and then helped others with their stories of healing with natural therapies, writing about their experiences and techniques. Some of those techniques have been recognized for thousands of years in other cultures, but deemed invalid in the States for a range of reasons. This creates the opportunity for patients to pick and choose what works, with different remedies effective for different individuals, at least that is what I have found.

All of my challenges—and there have been many in the past twenty years—were gut wrenching, life altering, and full of bizarre events, seemingly coming from "out of the blue." Often the answers came from the same Source. I will share those stories as well. I found it was wise to "listen" to the guiding voices in my head. It was proven to me that if I did not, I would get "thumped" on the back of the skull, figuratively and sometimes literally. Those thumps got my attention.

Fear is a part of my life, but not often, if I am willing to see that all of Life is in service to me, just as I am in service to all of Life. Read the book Pronoia – How The Whole World is Conspiring To Shower You With Blessings.

Focusing on "what works" helps me more than focusing on what doesn't. What works for me is uncovering options, practicing patience and acceptance, and believing there are gifts in all things. I stay, for the most part, centered on the positive side of this life, and how to love every single person. I feel strongly about Life as Universal Love, but one can translate that into any "religious language" they so choose. Faith in whatever you believe is exactly the point.

Regarding the intuitive "hits" I get; if they are calm, I will listen, and if they are not, I will not. You will find more information about this in the book, but a story might help.

One time I was driving down a street, preparing to turn left onto another street. About a block before making the turn the message came, "You could slow down if you wanted," to which I listened. The message was open, it was calm, and I had the choice.

While looking over my shoulder to turn left, instead of putting the pedal to the metal like I would usually do, I waited. Since I was waiting, I looked straight ahead to see a man walking directly in front of my car! If I had been in "let's get there" mode, I would have hit him. So, I listen if ideas are soft. If they are over the top, I assume it is just Fear talking and yes, I ignore it.

The bottom line is:

Intuition lights the path to healing if we trust our own opinion first.

CHAPTER ONE

Tap, Tap, Tap!

Base Beliefs

"Get to the closest hospital, now. Your blood levels are critical!" The woman on the phone was annoyingly insistent, and interrupting my busy day at the office.

It was March 14, 2010. Only three hours earlier I'd presented my naked arm for a blood draw. My friend Kathy—a nurse for nineteen years and friend for forty— urged me to get tested. For what, I was unsure, but Kathy was concerned about the tiny red dots spotting my legs and feet, a symptom called *petechiae*. Several large bruises had also formed on my legs over the past month, darkening Kathy's otherwise happy features with concern. It didn't seem like a very big deal to me, but better to be safe than sorry, she said.

My anxious caller was little more than a speed-bump in my demanding schedule. Fifty-eight years of life had convinced me things were seldom what they seemed, and that I could survive just about anything.

After all, I had been hatched in crisis. Before I was two, my sister, Wilda, twelve years my senior, had been in a near-fatal accident that Mother believed was her fault. Wilda, at just fourteen had had a "gut" feeling that she, for some reason, should not go to camp that fine June morning. She was listening to her intuition but our mother was not.

Despite Wilda's begging and pleading, Mother was bound and determined to see her go. She had already sent the check.

Of the six girls in the car accident that day, Wilda was the only one who made it out with her life. Since this story was told to me repeatedly through the years, it may have been the first use of intuition that I was aware of.

Unfortunately, Wilda lived the rest of her days with a limp, and Mother with a penchant for alcohol that never entirely succeeded in stifling her guilt. As a seamstress, she was what you would call a "working drunk," and attended to alterations in the small storefront of our home, a 14x16 foot rectangle divided into three areas: kitchen, bedroom and living room. The shower stall—a tall, metal cracker box—was in the living room part. Each day I made my own food for breakfast (mayonnaise sandwich) packed a lunch (ketchup sandwich), marched to school a mile each way, and returned exhausted.

As is usual for children of alcoholics, I was given responsibility for all manner of things early in life because mother was not often physically nor mentally available. The daughter of a master-manipulator, I became a very good one myself. This sometimes involved playing dumb, planning ahead or simply keeping my mouth shut. Mine was not a happy childhood by any means, with daily bouts of physical and mental abuse, but I maintained a positive outlook despite the fact I felt definitively,and ultimately, alone.

Years later a tragedy would strike our family, involving my son, David, that made Wilda's accident seem like a trip to Disneyland. The experience would convince me I had survived the worst pain one might encounter in a single lifetime; nothing could be harder. You will hear his story also, dear reader.

At the time of David's accident, a wonderful guide appeared to me in a dream. His name was Meshach. He said I would emerge from the "fires" of my life, without being burned. I knew then that I would be able to handle all that life had tossed at us. Meshach often returned with this reminder when I needed it most.

On the phone that day, my harried nurse was dropping her blood test bombshell on someone who had already lived through the equivalent of Hiroshima.

I hung up and finished my paperwork, delegated some tasks to my assistant and finally made my way to the car with an annoyed clip to my step. Managing my husband's counseling practice part time kept me busy, and I couldn't believe that yet another hour of my life was about to be squandered between sterile white walls.

I arrived at the small hospital close to my office. They were prepared for me, the lab having informed them of my imminent arrival. It was like most medical institutions; people skittered back and forth, beds filled and emptied, the staff fuelled by coffee, cigarettes and lingering vestiges of goodwill.

Almost immediately, I found myself whisked into the emergency room and tucked into bed, closely followed by the prick of an IV. My blood levels were so low the staff insisted upon a blood transfusion, and I looked at them in shock.

Weren't those reserved for accident victims and hemophiliacs, for folks with broken bodies hovering at death's door? I felt fine, ready to go back to work if they'd let me. They didn't let me, and I acquiesced. The staff seemed to be on a roll, and I've never been one to break up a party.

As they rushed around importantly, I formulated my own explanations of what was taking place. Had there been some nationwide blood surplus, and they were trying to push the stuff on everyone? Or perhaps this was a commonplace event, with many people needing a "refill" now and then...

"What's your blood type?" asked the nurse.

"O positive."

"Any allergies we should know about?"

"No."

"Relatives with low blood pressure, or low blood levels?"

I thought for a moment. "Yes, we all have low blood pressure, but we don't have low blood levels."

As the questions continued, I started to feel fatigued.

"Ms. Collins, we need to take your blood again before we give you a transfusion. Transfusions are for people getting their blood cleaned or changed in some way. In your case, we need to get more into your system, you could call it an infusion," the nurse explained.

I laughed, half deliriously. "Are you taking it out or putting it in? This better not be some kind of insurance scam!" I hoped to attract a chuckle and break the heavy tension in the room, but the woman only looked at me as if I were halfway to the madhouse. Perhaps I was.

I called my husband, Bill, to let him know what had happened and assure him there was no need to rush over. I've always had little tolerance for alarmists, unless there's a shoe sale involved.

The nurses took seven vials of blood then came back for more after having apparently "forgotten" some. When they returned for another two vials, I started to wonder. A moment ago, they had been saying my blood levels were dangerously low, and now they wanted to drain me of whatever was left!

Over the ensuing months I would learn it was common for staff to forget vials (or more accurately, the associated tests they were needed for) and that getting stuck multiple times was unavoidable.

On this day, my blood was not "running" well, and it took longer each time. Polka dots of large and small bruises began to appear on my arms. I stared at the dots in amazement. What exactly was happening in my body?

Satisfied, they now started the blood drip to fill me back up again. One nurse reclined the top of my bed slightly, and I managed to achieve something close to a sense of peace. The nurse pulled the curtain and dimmed the lights, and I felt the worries of the day slip into unconsciousness. This was obliterated ten minutes later when someone erupted with a loud, obnoxious hacking cough. I was rather surprised to realize it was me.

The attack started as sporadic, but the coughing refused to stop. As I reached for the nurse's buzzer my world tipped around me.

The nurse arrived and promptly called for the doctor. He turned up the lights and pulled back the curtain, declaring that I was having an allergic reaction to the blood. It was at this moment my husband walked into the room.

He would later tell me what he saw: my face puffed-up and blotchy, chest heaving as I fought to breathe through swollen airways. So much for my repeated assurances of no need for concern. But it was the start of a journey that would return us to our darkest hours, pushing us right back to a precipice we thought we had escaped.

The physician called for the nurse to bring medicine, which he then administered through my IV. Within minutes the coughing ceased and I was able to breathe again. Two hours later the sack of blood, and another filled with platelets, had finished draining into me. I was exhausted. They were willing to let me go.

The nurse passed me a number for a hematologist who would monitor me ongoing, and once home, I obediently made an appointment to see him the following day.

The rollercoaster ride had officially begun.

The next day I found myself in his office, baring my spotty legs. With a dash of pride I rattled off the medical term for the condition, expecting a pat on the head for doing my homework. Instead I was met with a frown.

"Chris, we don't know what's going on here. I strongly suggest you get blood and platelets infused every two to three days, until we do."

I nodded as he gravely continued. "And we need to do some tests. There's something called a "bone marrow biopsy" and it sounds awful, but trust me, it's not." As he picked up a six-inch needle, I tended to disagree. "You lie on your stomach, and we use this little guy to retrieve some marrow from your hip."

"Uh-huh." Turned out I *could* be a woman of few words after all. "I should be able to make time next week..." I ventured.

"Today would be best."

Still in a state of semi-shock, I trudged across the hospital. Everything was happening so quickly, and I could feel whatever control I thought I'd had of my life slowly slipping away.

A kindly technician awaited my arrival.

"It's really not painful, and we will be done in an hour, with an hour in recovery." He gave me a local anesthetic and a "happy" pill, which didn't alleviate my fear so much as suppress the embarrassment of lying prostrate with my backside exposed. He told the truth. It wasn't painful, and I was instructed to return a couple of days later to go through the results.

As I drove home I gazed at the traffic around me, remembering the driving rule I'd been taught about merging when I was sixteen. Apparently, it was best to remain focused on the car in front, waiting for them to move. Then, and only then, one might concentrate on the lanes into which you needed to merge. In that moment I decided to focus on what was in front of me: family, work and household chores. I wouldn't move into a scary place until the test results gave me some idea of the direction I would be taking.

These came sooner than anticipated, but without the answers I'd hoped for.

"Chris, the bone marrow test did not show much blood at all, and quite frankly, we're at a loss." So said the doctor on the phone.

My inner-fortitude slumped. Right away I was back in traffic, waiting for the chance to move forward, and choking on the fumes.

I was advised to continue getting the blood transfusions, and as I had no other option, I agreed.

The truth was, I had been on a downward course for fourteen years, and part of me couldn't believe my health hadn't deteriorated sooner. The past year had been particularly brutal, and I often felt I could no longer play the crappy hand I had been dealt. Nothing seemed to work. I dropped things, forgot to pay bills, missed appointments, walking around the house in a kind of stupor. Gazing into an empty fridge, I settled for a sugary treat and launched off to a happy place for an hour, only to crash back into dark ruminations on what could have been, or could never be.

In many ways, I had a death wish, a small, silent prayer to Life, begging that the charade be over, asking for a ticket to join my mother and father in the endless quiet.

Now it seemed that Life had decided to answer—quite literally draining the blood from my body. I grew impatient. Couldn't I have been hit by a bus, or caught in an unseasonal snowstorm? Instead I'd been bestowed a rare, nebulous condition, and I am not by definition a half-hearted person. Dead or alive, I was not going to settle for something in between.

"Kathy, they're puzzled," I said, calling the nurse-friend who had instructed me to get tested in the first place. "I don't know what to do, but it seems serious."

Straight away, she advised me to go to a larger hospital, one with a bigger staff and better facilities. I called the hematologist's office and got a referral to the "best blood doc" in town.

It was March 17, 2010, so I wore my Pot of Gold button—the Irish symbol for good luck. Despite everything I'd encountered in life I remained convinced that I was, in fact, lucky. It seemed a strange conundrum, to have thoroughly lost my zest for living, while at the same time knowing that gifts of epic proportion, like love from my husband and children, surrounded me like a warm blanket daily.

The worst physical pain I experienced was a migraine after consuming a large block of chocolate. Emotionally, I had also watched the lives of those dearest to me crumble. To me, the little gold button symbolized luck in both its beauty and ugliness, and in many ways I was still that little girl struggling through hard circumstances, unable to wipe the smile off her face.

However, I was tired of fighting. Somehow, I knew I was entering my final battle, and I would either walk out of it renewed, or surrender to it peacefully. It was life and death, but it was win-win all the same. I could only hope that either way, I might get my resolution quickly.

The next day I headed to the new hospital and, before long, was shown to a private room. After a few minutes a nurse's aide poked her head in. "Do you need anything? The doctor will arrive shortly."

She did that four times in two hours.

I had grown familiar with the hospital system over the past fourteen years, and learned to form connections with the staff to humanize my experience. Sometimes this resulted in wonderful friendships, but most of the time the line was dead. This time around, I found my usual jokes had "left the building."

I might have changed, but the system had not. It still demanded that I surrender my body to workers who were more troubled by record keeping and towing the political line than befriending the flesh on the end of their needles. This fundamental lack of trust meant that I entered the process unconvinced I would be cared for, or supported, and it was not conducive to healing.

Unable to seek solace in the external, I turned inward to meditation, a tool I had used for years to keep me in balance, calm, and clear on what I needed. The simple, soothing practice had saved me from going mad in the past, and I called upon it to guide me through the unchartered waters that lay ahead. There were times when the voice in my head actually suggested I stop and meditate. Sometimes I listened, sometimes I suggested back to the voice that I had my own ideas, thank-you-very-much.

On one occasion ten years previous, I'd been told by the voice to sit down on the living room couch, close my eyes, and get quiet and peaceful. Since it was the dead of winter, the snow drifting down in front of me, I declined. I wanted to go out and walk around the house, taking in the beauty and peace. Again, I was "told" to sit.

I grabbed my coat, threw it on, and took off into the beauty of a winter scene. That was until I, rounding the corner of the house, hit a patch of ice lying in wait and did a banana peel fall straight onto my back.

Now I had a perfect view of the snowflakes; they were coming straight down into my face. Yes, it was quiet all right, there were no neighbors out. They would have been helpful because I found that I was, basically, unable to move. With the impending realization I was in a pickle, I couldn't help chuckling inside, knowing that I could be warm, comfortable and content, if I had only listened to my "voice."

Eventually I was able to get up on all fours and get back into the house. From that point on I agreed that if I got that type of an intuitive "hit," I would not ignore it. Eventually I would even ask for the name of whomever was talking to me, and surprisingly, I got answers.

Within the quiet of the hospital room I began to wonder and create. I could now stay present, and in that moment, there was safety. I looked up at the ceiling, my mind floating, and imagined how nice it would be to fashion ceiling tiles that looked like clouds.

Just as I had forgotten about the doctor's imminent arrival, tap, tap, tap.... She walked in.

CHAPTER TWO

The First Call

Shock

It was September 25, 1994, fourteen years before life would descend into a circus of blood transfusions, mystery prognoses and baffled specialists. For us, a trip to the doctor meant a check up with the friendly MD, and hospital dramas were reserved for Friday night TV. The kids were reaching adulthood, and Bill and I sensed our focus shift as life transitioned into a new phase of freedom.

My son David was, by anyone's impression, an extremely handsome seventeen year old. He had three girlfriends, a Jeep, and the kind of smile that got him out of all sorts of trouble with his mother (and girlfriends). Small for his age until his sophomore year, David's senior year had marked his transformation into a six-foot wall of muscle and pent up energy. He was as comfortable on skis as he was on the football field, and in many ways defined by his physical self. It was hard not to admire him, bounding around the driveway each night, a peculiar blend of grace and strength as the basketball in his hands moved almost telepathically. Despite his size, however, he still slept under his bunk bed to enjoy the cool air from the floor vent, six years old again as his face relaxed in slumber.

When I heard the vague sound of sirens near our house, I didn't think much of it, but an hour later came a call that would change all our lives, forever.

The hospital chaplain spoke of a nightmare so unthinkable I refused to accept it as real. It had to be a mistake! As Bill and I rushed to the hospital, our initial denial transformed into a single prayer that we wouldn't find David dead upon our arrival.

The accident had occurred only three doors from our house. We were told by the ER staff that the only reason our son was alive was thanks to an anesthesiologist driving behind him at the time of impact. The man had administered critical medical attention and David had managed to hold on, somehow.

We waited while our son was in surgery, still finding it hard to believe that somewhere beyond the endless white walls his battered body was fighting to stay with us. As the hour passed I slipped into an almost meditative state, and from the great unknown the following words settled upon me:

"He will not die. His body will heal, but not the brain. That problem will be large."

Eyes closed I asked, "How long will it take?"

The words whispered through me. "It is open-ended."

Ten minutes later the surgeon walked out to confirm what I already knew.

"David has broken ribs front and back, he has a broken collar bone, and his spleen was ruptured and had to be removed. He will heal from those injuries with time." The man looked down, studying his notes as if to find the best way to say what had to come next. "You need to know that he also has a severe brain injury. He's in a coma, and we can't say what the long-term effects may be."

My husband, Bill, slumped in the seat beside me as I held my head in my hands, reality slowly breaking through our fog of disbelief.

We began the fall of 1994 within those hospital walls, twelve hours a day standing over David's bed as we watched for every breath, every sign of change. We took copious notes, and friends and family visited and took turns note-taking as well, all in the vague hope we might glean some small hint of recovery.

Nothing happened.

Day after day he lay unconscious, breathing through a hole in his throat, unaware of our constant vigil. It didn't matter. He was our only son, and just as we had watched over him in his first days of infancy, we found ourselves at his bedside once more, praying for him to return to us.

We endured the sad looks from the doctors and nurses, entering the room in constant rotation. We watched as David's temperature spiked and staff put him on a cooling mattress, full of frigid water. His brain was trying vehemently to organize his body back into order, but nothing it was trying seemed to work. All we could do was wait, but as I said, I've never been a patient person.

After the first two weeks, I had to act.

The first moment I had alone with my son, I did something I knew Bill would not necessarily agree with. I had read how a famous healer, Roger LaBorde, brought people out of comas and I longed to give it a try. I didn't plan to take it far—it was more an experiment than anything, and one sure to attract the ire of those closest to me.

I sat on a washable leatherette chair in the corner of David's hospital room with my eyes closed and feet on the floor, accepting no thoughts but the idea of connecting with my son. I really had no idea what "connecting" meant, so I simply reached through the dark, empty space in the hope of sensing some sign of him.

For minutes, nothing happened, and then a slight burning sensation heated my wrist. Concentration broken, I rubbed at the skin, glancing at my son across the room. A large splint ran from his elbow to palm, and I felt the skin prickle upon my neck. Walking to him, tentatively, I lifted his hand and glanced at flesh beneath. It was rubbed almost raw. Tears blurred my eyes as I unstrapped the splint, massaging the soft skin around the wound with my thumb.

Leaning closer, I spoke to my son during each of his out-breaths, just as LaBorde had suggested.

"David,
this is Mother.
I want you to know,
that we love you.
You have been in a
car accident.
The things which
were broken
have now been fixed.
But you have been
sleeping for quite a while.
I need to talk to you
about something important.
You have the ability
to make a decision.
We would like you
to stay on this earth
with us."

The machines beeped and whirred, but we hovered in a vacuum of our own, cloaked in silence. The next words were harder to summon.

"We will understand,
if you want to go on,
to the other side, sweetheart.
But if you want to stay,
you need to open your eyes,

or give some sign,
to let us know."

Within twelve hours, I saw my son's clear, green eyes for the first time in weeks. We were ecstatic. He was a long way from healed, but at least we had something to work with. David had decided to stay.

CHAPTER THREE

News I Couldn't Use

Shock

David's accident was life changing for all the wrong reasons, but it did prepare me for the moment I would have to enter the medical system fourteen years later for myself. I now knew there were "levels" to be ascended; you didn't just walk in and talk to the best specialist in town. Gatekeepers had to be circumvented, endless uncomfortable tests suffered, and a whole dictionary of medical jargon learned before you could graduate to the next level.

I was very much at the bottom rung of the ladder, and the doctor I was meeting with seemed similarly unconfident. Slightly built and a bit nervous, she looked, distractedly, for her pen only seconds after placing it in her hip pocket. Her eyes darted back and forth between her clipboard, myself and around the room. I wondered if she'd lost something else, like her wits.

"We don't know exactly what you have," she said finally, "but it *might* be very serious."

I can usually handle bad news or, in this case, no news with devastating possibilities. It took a lot to rattle me—Mother had provided some solid early training. Negative circumstances were never a result of *her* blunders, but mine, Grandmother's or most often, my absent father's. I accepted that I made her mad, but since it happened so often I eventually came to the conclusion that it couldn't be my fault *every* time. So I learned how to suppress the impact of blame, guilt or plain bad luck; if someone had a negative announcement to make, I took it with a grimace and a nod.

"It could be leukemia," continued the doc. "That's a worst-case scenario."

It was a stab in the dark and we both knew it. I didn't have a history of blood disorders in my family, and I didn't feel sick.

"Well, that's the bad news. What's the good news, the best-case scenario?" I asked.

Cue the crickets.

From her blank reaction, I felt that she was not going to be the person to guide me through the challenges ahead. It was time to move on, but before I could leave, her eyes darted back to the clipboard. "Also, Ms. Collins, the biopsy done at the other hospital could not be verified by this hospital."

I looked at her quizzically. It wasn't as if we were doing an international bank transaction.

"We'll have to perform another."

My nails bit into my palms, the mask of indifference taking a second longer to slip into place. In the hospital system, it is important to pick your battles.

"Okay, let's do it."

They moved me to a hospital room and prepped me for the procedure, this time administering a general anesthetic at my request. If I was going to get jabbed again, I was going to have the best time possible.

When I woke up I felt great, ready to paint the town red. It was a novel experience because I don't drink, and as I lay in recovery I struck up a fun conversation with the nurse.

"Whoa, these meds must be bestsellers."

"That's what they all say, but I saw the bottle of J.B. under your bed."

I laughed as if it were the funniest thing I'd ever heard, and with that over-the-top laughter, the room started to spin. My nurse proved a fair-weather friend as she handed me the spit pan and dashed out of the room to avoid the impending mess. Bill came in as she made her way down the hall, and he calmly talked me through the following hour of digestive purging. It was a valuable, if unpleasant, learning experience. I now knew to "Say No to Drugs," choosing local anesthetics whenever possible.

The next day I returned to see the chief hematologist, my appointment scheduled for one o'clock. I arrived at midday. I had moved up a level in the hospital hierarchy, and I wasn't going to be late.

When one o'clock rolled around, I found myself seated across from a handsome doctor, his cursory smile quickly lost behind the sheath of papers from my file, written in Urdu for all I knew. He didn't ask me how I felt, but if he had he would have been met with, "Well, I feel a bit like an old, bruised banana. I've lost twenty pounds, my hair's thinning and this whole floating thing takes time to get used to. It's like my head is a helium balloon, bouncing along behind my body. Could just be that I'm exhausted, but I have to care for my totally disabled son, so rest isn't really an option. In fact, I guess it doesn't really matter how I'm feeling, because how I feel doesn't change a thing."

My imaginary consultation complete, the doctor placed the papers down and fixed his dreamy blue gaze upon me. "Ms. Collins, I can confirm that you have a rare blood disorder. It affects only three people out of a million, which is why we had trouble diagnosing it. The condition is called Aplastic Anemia or AA."

I nodded, my heartbeat quickening as the faceless enemy was suddenly not so faceless.

"There are four critical problems associated with the disease, all having to do with blood counts. Your white and red blood cells, hemoglobin and platelets are all low or critically low." He went on to explain that if I were in an accident or lost blood for any reason, I would need to get a blood transfusion immediately. There simply wasn't enough juice in my body; my hemoglobin count was at 8 when the normal range was from 12 to 20; my red cell count was at 3 instead of 4 to 5; and my white cell count at 2 instead of 4 to 11. And platelets, well, they had called in sick, coming in at 11 when the normal range was 140 to 400.

"How, exactly, did I get to this point? How did my blood numbers get so low?"

"Could be many reasons," he replied.

"What are the possibilities?"

"I really couldn't say."

I wilted, the enemy slithering from my grasp and back into the shadows, just when I thought I might finally get some answers. He must have registered my dejection.

"Don't fret Ms. Collins. We work with this problem all the time."

I looked at him, frowning. You didn't need to be a mathematician to know that our city is comprised of almost two million people, which means that the good doctor might encounter less than ten individuals of "my kind," over this entire year.

"If possible, we need to get a bone marrow transplant from a family member who's under forty, but not a child."

"I don't have anyone like that."

"Then, we look at immunosuppressive therapy or IST. For a week we would give you drugs via a port in your chest, cleaning out your immune function before restarting the system."

I blinked, wondering if the doctor was still speaking about my treatment or if the conversation had somehow diverged into boat maintenance without my noticing.

That was nowhere near a reasonable solution. Does the body need a virtual war to heal?

The lights in the room were hurting my eyes and I longed to close them. All this news I couldn't use, each new option seeming worse than the last.

"Will I be sick during the treatment?"

"You might have a fever or reactions like the one you had from the blood transfusions, but on the whole it's better than the alternative. It won't kill you," he said.

If he expected a laugh, he didn't get one.

"For the next two years we'll also continue with regular blood transfusions, and hopefully you'll have a full recovery."

I imagined spending another two years in hospital rooms and shuddered. "What happens if I don't do the IST therapy?" I asked.

"Then I'd give it three to six months" he said.

I perked up. "For recovery?"

"No..." His bright blue eyes softened. "...for death."

I stared at him in disbelief, unable to entertain the possibility that my life could end before I received my next water bill. There had to be some mistake, a botched test or a handsome doctor who had failed his exams and slept his way to the top. Anything but *three to six months.*

Somewhere deep inside there were two small doors. I knew I would not be walking through one of them. I forgot about them as soon as they appeared to me and came back to reality in a blink.

The countdown had begun.

CHAPTER FOUR

He Begins Again

Choice

The hospital staff cautioned us that it would be some time before David was up and walking again. Given the extent of his injuries, that was only to be expected. But what constituted "some time"? Weeks, months, maybe even years? We found out later that they simply didn't know, but no one wanted to admit it at the time. We hung on to any and every word from the personnel, reminding ourselves that while the experience was shattering to us, they had been through it all before.

At that point, David was considered to be in "open-eyed coma." He was awake, but couldn't repeat any movement voluntarily, and after three months of therapy with scant improvement, we were presented with a choice: either move him to a nearby nursing facility or bring him back home. Bill and I looked at each other, the answer confirmed in the hope—and terror—flashing through our eyes. We took upon the challenge with no hesitation. We were no longer just parents. We were now caregivers, nurses, on call 24/7. We just didn't know it.

There was help, however, from the inner voices.

We were planning on how to care for David and arranging for all the things that were needed. Hospital bed, check. Disposable diapers for adults, check. What about all the things we had to have for his two belly tubes? What about keeping him clean, comfortable, all of those little things that I had to keep in one place so they would be handy? I told Bill what we really needed was a "three level plastic roundy-round thing" that we could see through and grab things quickly. He suggested I go and buy one. I said, "No, silly...I don't know where to buy something like that, I was just saying that we could use it. It would be so cool to have it." I'm sure he looked at me like I was nuts, as old married people often look at each other.

I was sitting at an intersection near a mall one day about three days before David was scheduled to return home. While waiting at the stoplight, a voice suggested that I go over to the mall. I knew it wasn't *my* voice because, well, I don't do retail. I commented back to the voice silently that I did not "get" it. The voice then suggested that I go over in the parking lot and meditate. Okay, I could do that. After about twenty minutes sitting in meditation, upon coming back "out," the voice said that I should go to the back of the mall, and I followed the thought.

When I got to the back of the mall, I was directed to go near a set of dumpsters. These were eight foot high dumpsters, no less. It said, go and climb up on it. I thought, *Are you kidding me? I can't do that!* But since I had asked to be led, I thought I might as well follow. Little by little, with glances over my shoulder hoping no one would see me, I climbed up the little metal rods on the corner. When I reached the top I found within my reach was a slightly cracked but very usable, three tiered Plexiglas Lazy Susan, my "three level plastic roundy-round thing." Well, I almost fell off my perch laughing at the sight. I knew I had help, perhaps not on this plane, but help was there nonetheless. Gifts like the Lazy Susan that appear just when you need them most I call Synchronistic Unusual Moments or SUMs.

Back in his old room, months later, David showed small glimpses of awareness, but nothing notable. One day in May, when we were going to play some movies, I mechanically held them up and asked, "Which do you want, this one or this?"

With a flick of the eye he signaled for the DVD in my left hand, and with a jolt I realized he'd been communicating his choices this way for a week, at least, without my even noticing. The unspoken communication had developed automatically.

If he could pick a movie, he could also communicate a whole lot more. I grabbed a dry erase board off the fridge and some markers. The letters were wobbly as I wrote them out, my hands trembling with excitement, but they were legible nonetheless:

A B C D E F G
H I J K L M N
O P Q R S T
U V W X Y Z

The thought of communicating with him again after so long, after so much shared anguish, filled my eyes with tears. Clearing my throat, I began.

"David, it's been eight months since you were last able to speak. Now you can say whatever you want. I am going to say each letter out loud, and you look up whenever I hit the right one. Then I'll write it below."

We began. It was grueling, my hands shaking and eyes watering as I watched for David's movements. I desperately hoped for some sign from the son I knew, and thought there was every chance I'd be faced with a long line of expletives. When the first letter came, I almost jumped out of my skin. Surprisingly, it wasn't an F.

"I."

I beamed, returning to the letters and reading them aloud to discover what followed.

"W.A.N.T."

My mind raced with possibilities. The euphoria of finally being able to give David what he wanted was so potent that my head spun. After eight months of silence, he was empowered with the gift of communication and my relief was almost as great as his own. The tears began to stream down my face as we continued.

"T.O."

"To..." I repeated softly, the word creeping to the front of my mind with a dark companion lurking at its heels. There were many things a seventeen-year-old boy might want to do. Go for pizza, meet up with friends or shoot some hoops. But David wasn't a seventeen-year-old boy anymore. He was a prisoner, trapped inside his own body. The next word was the last any mother would ever want to hear, and yet it was the only one he could reasonably be expected to give.

"D.I.E."

With the "E" scribbled halfheartedly on the board, I looked up to find Bill standing in the doorway, his face white with shock. My husband stepped toward me and began to sob, the two of us sinking next to David in his hospital bed as we wept together. David couldn't move nor speak, but the tears flowed freely from his eyes, all three of us broken hearted.

The reality of his hopelessness was a painful pill to swallow, but a door had opened to a world of new possibilities. Now he could tell us what he wanted to eat, when he was feeling pain, if he had an itch he couldn't reach—the smallest trivialities right up to life-defining needs.

Two weeks later, he spelled out a message that made me rush through the house, screaming for Bill.

"*I no longer have a death wish.*"

And with that, our lives went on.

David learned to use his feet to propel his wheelchair, but he didn't have use of his hands, arms or the ability to stand upright without two people to assist. Bathing took time, as well as dressing, and his bed sheets and clothes needed to be changed often. Once he was clothed in the morning, I would drain formula and water into his body via two stomach tubes, which would often dislodge from the formula bag, resulting in another change of clothes and linens. Of course, this process would come to a grinding halt whenever the need to spell words arose.

Bill and I took turns caring for David, caught up in a constant rotation of feeding, massaging tight leg muscles, dressing, laundry and washing, occasionally stopping to make food for ourselves whenever possible. But it wasn't often. We had little interest in food.

After six months, Bill needed to return to full-time work, and I had to find caregivers to help throughout the day. Each Thursday evening Kathy would miraculously appear on my doorstep, a true blue friend who would look after David so Bill and I could catch a moment alone. Friends would visit with meals and care packages, but they had their own lives to live, and it was hard for them to face the young, silent man in bed when so many remembered the vibrant person he had been.

Through therapy, he learned how to eat and drink again, and the stomach tubes were eventually removed. We became organized and efficient in our care, but it was still a 24/7 job and one that challenged and strengthened us every day. The growth of our strength was essential, as more tough times would follow.

The Gathering

When struck down by hardship, it is amazing to witness the help and care that springs from nowhere. I will always remember the mothers of other brain-injured people who came to coach us on how to shortcut the most time-consuming tasks. Lord knows how they discovered us, but they did. Small tricks they shared revolutionized our day-to-day operations, such as how to dress a feeding tube easily, manipulate the hospital bed to our advantage, and the best ways to move David in and out of his wheelchair.

My intuition was also helpful; it was like there was a rhythm to life and all I had to do is get into that rhythm and the day would rock and roll. I began to see that assistance could be found everywhere I looked. This was a good thing; I needed all the help I could get.

One friend, Sandra, worked in a nursing home and was full of good tips when it came to care for the disabled. She also had experience with depression, an ailment just as serious as any physical incapacity, but quite a bit harder to talk about. I decided to trust her with the thoughts I found most difficult to share.

"Why am I not happy, Sandra?"

"What do you mean?" she replied.

"David is able to 'speak' again and I should be happy but I feel like a wet rag being wrung out constantly."

"What thoughts or feelings come up?"

"Oh, I don't know," I said, waving my hand in dismissal. "All day I wonder if I'm doing the right thing by David. Will he get better? Will he get worse? How long will this last..." I held my head in exasperation, each question more frustrating than the last.

"I hear you", she said. "It sounds like you have been taking in a lot of pain for some time now. Maybe it's time to let it back out."

"You mean crying? That's what I *don't* want to do!"

She nodded and allowed me the time I needed. I thought about it, and what it meant to open myself up in that way.

"What if I never stop?"

"I don't think that will happen, Chris," she said, smiling. "But it does take work to release anger, fear and pain."

She went on to tell me about the Screaming Rooms of Japan, where frustrated clients went to break furniture, smash vases, shout obscenities and let loose. Apparently, it had proven a successful type of therapy for adults, and there was even an Anger Room in Dallas.

"But you don't need to go to anywhere Chris, you can do it right here."

I pictured Bill coming home to find me setting fire to the curtains, David wheeling his chair through broken crockery, and a bloodied aide cowering in the corner.

"I'm not so sure," I said.

"You need to release it somehow; cry, sob, scream, curse, whatever feels like coming up. It's like a good thunderstorm, violent for a moment, but then incredibly calming once it's passed."

I reluctantly agreed to try it, and we sat down to work out a plan. My son had occasional therapy appointments where he left the house for two hours at a time. It was on those days that I would go down to the basement and "release." But release what, I wasn't sure.

When the big day came I was prepared. Initially, I didn't feel like crying, but I went through the motions somewhat in jest, chuckling because it felt so ridiculous.

I took a thick beach towel, rolled it up and used it to smack one of the steel support posts. At first it was all play acting, and I found it hard to get into the role. After a few swats, however, Sandra's words returned to me.

"Yell at whomever you want, tell them what you think of this unfair situation. Curse them no matter who they are, dead or alive, and say whatever it is you really want to say. Scream it, growl it, spit it out...then let it go."

I took the towel in both hands and spread my feet for stability. As I began hitting the post from the right, and then the left, I felt the heat coming up through my soles and into my core. With it came the horrendous pain I had lived with for months.

I *was* mad, it *was* unfair, and I was going to tell someone how I felt. The first victim in my mind: God Himself. For the next twenty minutes I swore and hissed, screamed, twisted and turned, until the towel had hit the post from every possible direction.

"This is NOT RIGHT! How could you do this to my beautiful son? He was just starting his life, when you completely obliterated it. What are you? What *are you*? You horrendous presence. You are A THIEF. A CHILD KILLER! You are a heartless bastard, you are... you are the DEVIL. That's right, you're the GODDAMNED DEVIL!" After several minutes of this and similar unforgivable blasphemy, I collapsed onto the floor, sobbing and utterly spent. The pain was out, and the space it left behind allowed me to take my first deep breath in almost a year.

I did this work every other day, verbally accosting all I thought who were at fault, from my parents to the doctors and everyone I could imagine. Sandra gave me no permission to blame myself. I did not understand why. After all, wasn't I probably a large part of the problem? Her question stopped me. "Can you tell me how that will help you?" Since I couldn't find an answer, I moved on. I needed to be a friend to myself – no matter what. And I made peace with Source as well. I knew that these feelings were all mine – no one else really did this to us. It all just happened, because it was all just Life.

The crying part took only five to twenty minutes, but the aftermath required me to lie down for at least a couple of hours. I would remain in a stupor for the rest of the afternoon, and sink into a deep sleep each night. But when I rose in the morning, the sun shone, the birds sang and I was more than ready to start the day.

Sometimes, mostly when I was in a buoyant mood and did not want to do the work, all I needed to do was pause for a moment and think back to our past life, or forward to our unknown future, and the pain would come. It seemed buried, but in truth it was never far away, and I learned that if I could keep my mind from wandering into the past or future, I could stay "even." The daily work of care giving kept me in the now, thankfully.

After a while, I found that I needed these releases only once a week, then only once every month, and finally only a few times a year. When I felt the emotions building up, or snapped at the grocery clerk for no good reason, I knew a trip to the basement was in order.

Learning how to release my negative and painful emotions saved my sanity, and probably the sanity of those around me, too.

My dear friend and coach, Sandra Hardcastle.

CHAPTER FIVE

Logic Will Come Later

Chaos

My eyesight was fine, but I couldn't see further than the desk on which I was leaning. The doctor's lips were moving, but his words were lost in a fog that refused to clear. I had reached The Wall.

I was familiar with The Wall, having spent some time trapped against it in the hours after my son's accident. Almost dreamlike, it was a limbo where time and space no longer held sway, and there was nothing to say or do. I could only wait for my mind to clear, for some part of my brain to switch on and realize that mental breakdowns weren't conducive to survival.

The doctors believed that my immune system was at war with itself, my cells caught up in some cannibalistic bloodbath. Gory, huh? They hoped the IST would stop all immune function in a cut, burn and poison approach, razing the village before rebuilding from the ground up. I didn't know it then, but one of the main differences between Western and Eastern medical practice is that Eastern philosophy is based on building up the system, so the body heals itself.

The doctor spoke in a comforting tone. "Sometimes these decisions require a little time. Why not focus on getting fresh transfusions, and if your blood numbers rise we'll be in a stronger position to continue with the IST."

"Okay, let's do it," I agreed, only to glance up and see that he'd already left. I'd probably been sitting there, staring at the floor for ten minutes. Thankfully I wasn't wearing a straight jacket, yet.

Just go through the motions, Chris, the logic will come later.

I couldn't understand what was happening, so I didn't try. To do so would have been a waste of time and energy. Besides, I had a sneaking suspicion I had more time than the good doctor thought. In many ways, my prognosis was hopeless, but beyond the doom of that reality was a small, flickering flame that refused to be extinguished. Somewhere out there existed an answer. I had functioned as a healthy human being for decades, and I refused to believe that my body had suddenly just "stopped working." Many would have called it that dreaded word denial, others intuition, but whatever it was, I knew that light was the only real hope I had.

A nurse arrived and walked me over to a room filled with around twenty recliners. Curtains hung between each patient, but no one had chosen to draw them closed. Women and men sat in silence hooked to their drips, some filled with blood, others with chemicals for chemotherapy. A few of the patients had family members sitting nearby, others—like me—were alone.

I didn't see the need for family or friends to be with me in times of medical puzzlement. I didn't want to make small talk or worry that someone else was worried. I couldn't bear to hear nervous laughter, always followed by, "You're going to be alright, you know." It wasn't comforting, but cringe-worthy.

Instead, I thought about David and his incredible bravery. These days it was rare for us to have to "re-sell" the need for him to keep going. When times were at their toughest, he, unable to walk, talk or feed himself, encouraged us. I whispered into the air, "David, send me some energy."

Sitting in a recliner, I took off my jacket and exposed my arm for the third time that week, repeating my name, birth date and blood type.

The young nurse had a tittering laugh, jabbing at my arm with an air of hopefulness, then frustration, and hopefulness once more as she picked a new vein. I could tell a novice from a veteran within the first thirty seconds, and I tried to will away my frustration. An experienced nurse would look at the arm, select where she planned to work, and then hold a silent kind of communication between herself and the flesh. As if by magic, the vein knew she meant business, and when the needle came it quickly surrendered to the process. The novice on the other hand, approached from the first moment with hesitancy. "Oh dear, I don't want to hurt you. Work with me, will you?" he or she would plead with my arm.

Eventually I learned to ask, "Are you good at sticks?"

"Well, not really."

"Then let's call in a veteran, shall we?"

Most times, the nurse gladly agreed, and as the job was done quickly and efficiently I would make a silent prayer: *Thank you nurses for your care, and this life-giving blood. Thank you, Life, for not dumping me in a third-world, blood-spattered hovel somewhere....* Evidently David had, indeed, sent me energy.

The gratitude continued as I laid back and closed my eyes. For all that had happened, there was so much to be thankful for. What if I hadn't been able to afford my treatments? Or had been past the point of no return? Expressing gratitude was the fastest way to calm my anxiety and maintain some sense of perspective. I was suffering, but I wasn't dead yet.

The only sounds I could hear were from the televisions lining each side of the room, each set to a different channel. Within twenty minutes, I began to cough. I raised my hand and the nurse knew what to do.

Evidently my body—like most others—did not appreciate being filled with another body's blood. This was solved by the Benadryl in my IV;

my system tricked into accepting a foreign substance. I became drowsy, my body capitulating even faster than the last time. After two hours I was free to go home.

Groggy, I propelled myself to the hospital garage, still wrapped in the haze of my meditative state. After practicing for twenty years, I had learned to "drop down" into meditation with ease, and sometimes I didn't even need to force a return to reality. It was automatic. This time, however, my mind refused to clear. Each step felt isolated, and with my head down I tottered along.

Where is my car? And more importantly, what does it look like? Twenty minutes later I found myself standing on the fourth level, marked by yellow, gazing at a patch of flowers in the garden below. I must have appeared as one of those mad old women, muttering to herself about cats and absent grandchildren, but in hindsight I realized that I'd gone into shock after hearing my prognosis. Eventually the meditation enabled me to get clear in the moment and disengage from the future, even if it was only for a short while. That mental clarity was founded on the acceptance of one thing: *Everything is perfect. There is no need to be concerned, only to live in this moment, then the next, as it happens.*

Putting one foot in front of the other was enough. The car appeared, and I sat inside as if it were an island in the middle of a raging ocean. I had no idea what to do next. It was the middle of the day and I didn't want to return to the office or face my husband. *Three to six months.* I could imagine Bill's expression as I gave him this news, as I'd seen desperation and hopelessness etched into his features too many times already. Having already been through Life-As-Hell, how in heaven's name could I do this to him today?

Intuitively, the thought came to drive to my friend Joanie's house and seek solace there instead. She had been a delightful teacher to me since the day I met her, one of those rare people who allow you to be you in their presence, just as you are, no other requirements.

One of the most important lessons Joanie had shared with me was as a result of her own life threatening illness. A few years prior, Joanie had been told by her M.D. that she had Crohn's Disease. Her immediate response was, "Oh no, that's not right." The physician repeated the test results, thinking she was suffering from denial. But it wasn't denial, rather a declaration. "No, I'm not accepting that."

When she called me with the news we talked at length, then began to research the problem and possible solutions. We called ourselves the "Edufrolics" because we had fun while learning, and often toasted our new best friend, the Internet.

We soon discovered that a key factor in Joanie's health was changing her vitamin supplements, months later she would find that changing her diet was also essential. She did so and her stomach problems reduced, her sense of wellbeing increased, and her confidence was reinstated. However her first step to recovery was telling her doctor she would not accept his diagnosis.

He ignored her comments and instructed her to start on prednisone, as well as a cocktail of other prescriptions. There was every chance, he said gravely, that she would need a wheelchair in her house as soon as possible. If she wasn't willing to heed his advice, he could no longer be her doctor. She accepted his resignation as her caregiver and never looked back. A full decade later, she continues to enjoy excellent health.

When I arrived at Joanie's house—likely pale as a ghost—I stumbled through the front door and murmured that I needed to lie down. Joanie didn't ask any questions, but simply led me to one of her bedrooms where I lowered myself onto the comforter and wept. It was a sizeable load, not the heftiest I have had, but enough to feel like a gut punch from a heavy-weight. I rested for thirty minutes and then got up to find her. She was in the kitchen, so I walked up and told my story. She hugged me while we both wept.

After we sat down, she looked me in the eye, quietly assessing. I breathed deep and awaited her advice.

"Chris, you know you don't have to accept what they are saying. This doesn't have to be your truth."

I shrugged, agreeing with her in theory, but struggling to see how it could be anything but my new reality.

"Here's the thing. Just because someone says you are going to die, it doesn't mean you have to. Remember that great line, "All the information *you have on me* does not trump all the information *I have on me*." The options are still open, and you have choice in this matter."

I thought of David, and knew he would say something along the lines of, "What are you afraid of, Mom? This is nothing, you'll be fine." A week later when we broke the news to him, that is *exactly* what he said.

Unlike Joanie, I did not feel strong enough to decline my diagnosis outright, but knew that her type of thinking was much more in line with what I was feeling.

There was this undeniable strength when I connected with my Source, whatever that was, and it had a consistency that did not waver. It's unfortunate that often it doesn't make much sense. I went home unsure of what to do, but I had more strength than I'd had an hour earlier, and that pea-size grain of conviction would grow into an oversized pumpkin before too long.

Most of us are familiar with a theory that was brought about years ago by a very famous physician. Psychiatrist Elisabeth Kübler-Ross formed the Stages of Grief model based on her observations of those struck down by a terminal illness, though she later expanded this to relate to any person suffering a catastrophic loss. The stages, popularly known by the acronym DABDA, include: Denial, Anger, Bargaining, Depression and Acceptance.

The application of the Kübler-Ross Model is intended to help sufferers fully resolve each stage before transitioning to the next, without becoming stuck. Ultimately, acceptance is the key to a peaceful death, or successful recovery, and this model has helped countless patients who are bound to the psychiatrist's couch and hospital bed.

This process is most useful for those who have surrendered themselves to the medical system; an often frightening and uncomfortable process. However an increasing number of people are choosing to look beyond diagnosis and "the doctor's orders," to adopt a more empowered approach to their healing. This can result in a different journey, one I present below as the "Stages of Reviving" and you see them at the start of each chapter:

Shock

There is no way to avoid the isolation of a terminal diagnosis. Life descends into a fog of confusion, everything slowing to one plodding step at a time.

The Gathering

Friends and family rush to assist as you struggle between needing their support and collapsing beneath the weight of their concern.

Chaos

Everything and nothing presents a solution, and you simply don't have the will or clarity to find a path forward. But intuitively, you know the answer is out there, somewhere.

The Dig

Mentors, other Revivors, the local library, and the blessed Internet come to the rescue, along with that first flicker of conviction.

Choice

Your life is at stake and choices must be made. Empowered, you choose your own road, stay open to all results and accept responsibility for the outcome.

Shift

Fear begins to recede as your body grows stronger. Yes, you can heal yourself.

New Life

In everyday life, you focus on what you truly enjoy to bring your physical, spiritual, and mental health into balance.

Most importantly, in both Kübler-Ross' model and my own, I believe a single fundamental worldview dictates how sufferers move through each stage. I call this their "**Base Beliefs**."

In Kübler-Ross' model, the Base Beliefs center around: "I am ill, and I must rely on others to tell me how to recover. I hand over all personal responsibility, and continue to place the wellbeing of others before my own. I do not have a strong history of success over tragedy. I am truly what 'they' say I am: a terminal patient."

In the Revivor model, a patient's Base Beliefs could be seen as, "I am not feeling well at this point in time. However, I have felt well in the past, and I remember that. Only I am responsible for my health, and right now it comes first. I have lived through challenges in the past, which I have not only survived, but benefitted from. I may take years to heal, just as it has taken years for me to decline. I have choices in each matter, but I accept a death sentence from no one. I am ready for anything; I am what I call myself, a Revivor." In the article "Researchers Finally Show How Mindfulness and Your Thoughts Can Induce Specific Molecular Changes To Your Genes" developmental biologist Dr. Bruce Lipton states that "your mind will adjust the body's biology and behavior to fit with your beliefs."

In both the Kübler-Ross' model and the Revivor model, steps can be skipped or repeated depending on the individual's unique experience. Therefore, both models are rough guidelines.

In mid-May—with two of my remaining three-to-six months gone—the hematologist's office called with a request to see me. It was not good news. I knew my body was getting weaker; a *whoosh-whooshing* sound followed me every minute of the day, in my ears, with every heartbeat. My weight was about 125 pounds and continued to drop, and my heart raced at 86 beats per minute when it should have been closer to 72. Walking was strategic. Unless I slowed my pace down to that of a 90 year old woman worn out after an afternoon with two toddlers, my chest pounded and I found it increasingly difficult to breathe, but I tried not to speak too much about these issues and few people asked.

"Mrs. Collins you are wasting time, and blood in my opinion," he said, frowning at my selfishness. "You need to get the port placed and undergo the IST now, while there's still time for it to take effect. The procedure will only last one week."

The problem was that many of those close to me had undergone hospital stays for terminal conditions: my mother, sister, mother-in-law, brother-in-law and friends. Their treatments had only led to more treatments, precious final days swallowed up by those white walls. I could almost see them in spirit parading in front of me, shaking their heads as if to say, "Get the hell out of there, Chris!"

Being used to this type of communication, I spoke and asked for help from my long deceased mother, father, aunt, grandmother and sister. I always got a response. However, talking to folks on the "other" side, one gets information in a subtle sense, and that is often confusing rather than clarifying. In any case, I liked being able to get *any* information from my loved ones, subtle or otherwise.

Their treatments years prior had included surgery, months of chemo and radiation. In comparison, my recovery path was a walk in the park: one week in the hospital for IST, a shutdown and restart of my immune system, then everything would be better. Simple, right?

But what if the good doc was wrong? I thought back to the first lesson I'd learned, years ago, as a volunteer in hospice training: There are no guarantees. Just as you couldn't guarantee someone's recovery, neither could you assert their death with 100 percent accuracy. Sure enough, some of the people I served in the hospice actually came out again because they got better.

I knew that I needed to shut up and give the doctors my body with a hope and a smile. As the patient, it was my responsibility to let "the machine" do its work. The problem was my fundamental lack of trust in the system; I couldn't go along with it. Not completely.

My body rejecting the fresh blood had been the first "sign" to appear, but others had followed. Even with the transfusions, my blood levels refused to budge. I was tested on a weekly basis, and it was always the same: zip to nada on the benefit scale. Didn't that tell me something?

Then there was the conversation I heard in the transfusion area. "Yeah, this port got infected," said the patient to his nurse, "and I had to have a new one put in." The young woman made some empathetic clucking noises as she went about tidying up his bed. "But I don't think this port is working either," he continued. "Maybe you can ask someone about it?"

She promised to talk to the doctor, and the patient, clearly exasperated, made a final plea. "This big hole in my chest…I can't sleep. Can I have something to help me sleep, at least?"

Perhaps the biggest sign of all was the gulf of distrust that existed between myself and the medical staff. My micromanaging, though helpful, did not instill a sense of security.

"No, that's not the right type of blood."

"I don't need the Benadryl until later, thank you."

"I believe I'm supposed to get platelets, not blood, this time."

Each time they had to go and check, and would inevitably come back to finish the job correctly.

They were kind enough—you'd have to be halfway to sainthood to perform roles like that, day-in and day-out—but with the constant rotation of shifts and schedules meant that I rarely had the chance to form deeper relationships.

The system functioned on the premise that caregivers and patients are interchangeable. It felt akin to what I imagine all patients must suffer: everyone acting the same, but the faces changing all the time. It was unsettling to imagine the possible consequences of this "disconnect," so I constantly kept up my guard.

CHAPTER SIX

Who You Gonna Call?

The Dig

Billions of dollars each year support allopathic research (the Western methodology of using drugs and surgery to suppress or remove symptoms) and I've always endorsed anyone who followed this path. It is the one most traveled in the free world, and modern medicine is a wonderful and miraculous thing. There is nothing like a good cardiologist when someone needs a cardiac cath, nothing like a good urologist when a bladder is infected with a nasty bug. However, when my terminal diagnosis was tossed out, I had to find alternatives because I felt mainstream medicine suited many, but not all. And not me.

When I was in my twenties and younger, I had several UTI's and was prescribed antibiotics. I accepted the direction of doctors who said, "Make sure you take all the medicine." However, a white film would appear on my tongue and it would hurt. It was called thrush and it was a clear sign that all the gut flora was gone. After calling the doctor's office, I would invariably be told to stop taking the medication because my tongue would only get worse. So I was familiar with inconsistent messages from the medical community.

Now I needed to discover what others with my problem were doing. Through the blessed Internet, there was plenty of information. I grasped it with both my spotty little hands and refused to let go, eager to discover possible lifelines.

At the start of this journey I spoke to my friend-turned-life-coach.

"Sandra, I am going to do some research on Aplastic Anemia, but I have a problem."

"What?" she asked.

"Maybe I don't *want* to know."

"Know what?"

"What it looks like, the symptoms it inflicts, how the disease runs its course, what it eats for dinner."

"Hmm." While we laugh together often, my sometimes silly turns of phrase confuse my dear friend Sandra.

"I want ambiguity," I continued. "In fact, I think ambiguity will be my new favorite word."

"You've never been what I would call an ambiguous person, Chris," she said. "In fact, I'd say you're crystal clear."

"Sure, but if I learn all about AA, my body will accept it, mirror it, and 'do' the disease quite well. I know myself, and that's how I work."

"Hmm," she said a second time. "Why not ask Life to help you on this? You just want information on how to heal, right?"

"Right."

"Well, ask for that and nothing else."

I smiled, reminding myself for the umpteenth time to order a bracelet with WWSD; What Would Sandra Do?

The next time I was in a meditative state, I asked lightly if I could be given the information I sought, and nothing more. Over and over, Life had proven to me that it listened when I asked, and at other times, it knew what I wanted long before I did. Once I'd stated my intention, I was ready to step into the void of the unknown. *Contuition* (solid confidence in my own intuition) was an almost constant source of calm.

I progressed through my research and the weeks passed, the countdown of months always hovering at the back of my mind. When the facts and data grew overwhelming, I turned to my mentors for support on both sides of the veil.

Long ago, I spent three weeks with a meditation teacher named Anna Wise. She was the epitome of internal wisdom. She helped me to understand how meditation was integral to staying centered, peaceful and tuned into the inner knowing that all of us have but few of us realize. She did not start me on my path to meditation, however she made the way concrete for me, and after she passed to the other side I asked if she would be a guide. She agreed. From then on, I was able to ask her how to gain more information and knowledge, where to look, how to dig. With her calm attitude, she showed me how to find the information I sought.

Even so, I sometimes forgot the lessons I'd learned. A great team player when all was smooth sailing, the moment storm clouds gathered I found it hard to include others in my struggle. To this day my brain functions differently (read: weird) to others, and I avoid being put in positions where I have to justify my actions or ask for permission.

My strength coach, Cynthia, was the one who had initially encouraged me to include more coaches and helpers in my journey. She explained that mentors were only there to offer ideas from a third-party perspective. That seemed reasonable and I was willing to give it a shot, soon discovering that to find one great coach or helper, I had to sift through two. While digging through this mysterious morass, I found that it was not a bad ratio. There were all types of assistance. Nurses, nutrition consultants, other physicians, other medical researchers, writers, and people who had healed themselves from illnesses previously thought impossible to recover from – those were gold.

Once I had interviewed them, if I felt we were a good fit I would try them out for a session or two. It was helpful just to share my story and see what thoughts popcorned between us.

I went back to Cynthia.

"Cynthia, I need to explore some ideas."

"I'm ready, shoot!"

"Some articles on the net say that people who have AA and do the IST therapy often have to do it again, if the first time doesn't 'take'," I said. "There isn't much data on the efficiency of the second round of treatment."

"Okay."

"Secondly, after they do the therapy, they completely change their diets, lives and stress levels. Some people even extract all the toxic elements from their bodies, homes and workplaces—they stay away from fumes, rip up old carpet, clear out molds..." I cast a desperate eye around our house, "Different soaps, clothes, foods...BIG changes."

"Great. Are you going to do all of that?"

"You know me, Cynthia. It's just not my style." And it wasn't; the whole thing smacked of fear. "I can't live like that. I'm not a neatnik by any means. Dad always said, 'You have to eat a bushel of dirt before you die.' I can't run from something I'm not sure exists, and spend money doing it!"

If Sandra liked to revert to "Hmm" on occasion, Cynthia's favorite expression was "Okay."

"Okay...What else did you learn?"

"Well, in other cultures, they work with illness differently, like Traditional Chinese Medicine, or TCM. They believe that if you build the body up, it will take care of anything that needs taking care of. They even have a hospital where you can go for three months and heal yourself!"

"Are you going to do that?" Cynthia asked.

"No, of course not," I scoffed, unable to imagine myself living in a Chinese hospital for months. "I can't afford it, and I can't be away from David for long. But I will keep searching. You never know what might come up."

"Okay, Chris. I'm with you."

After promising to keep Cynthia updated, I hung up and thought about what we'd discussed. I was cautiously optimistic, at best. But what I found next would shift the tide of my life completely.

CHAPTER SEVEN

A Crack In The Wall

Choice

It was now the end of June, three months into my three-to-six month sentence, and things were deteriorating fast. I couldn't hold a phone for more than a minute or two, and I had an arduous time blow-drying my short hair; my hands and arms falling asleep as soon as I used them. Mouth sores appeared and lasted for weeks at a time now, making it painful to talk. I could still drive myself around, but my body felt heavy. Sinking into fear for ninety percent of my day, I wept often. Once upon a time I would have laughed and said, "Give me twenty Kleenexes and I can get through anything!" By now, a box of tissues was simply the first step to getting out of bed in the morning. Fear was erecting walls of concrete, one large block at a time. Where oh where was my pink painted diamond encrusted twenty five pound sledgehammer?

Invoices were starting to come in, and for every transfusion, our co-pay was $200 or more. With tests, consultations and transfusions occurring twice a week at least, the bills were already well into the thousands.

Traditional Chinese Medicine was interesting, but my first line of defense was meditation. It had already saved my life once before, because if it weren't for my sitting practice there was no way I could have survived being the mother to a brain-injured, totally dependent young man for fourteen years. With this in mind, each day I took time to sit. I had a wobbly chair next to my desk, but it was strong enough to hold me, and I faced the sun. Breathing deeply, I would think of my intention for that day, paper and pen nearby for all the ideas and reminders I needed to clear out of my mind. When the flow of thoughts had ended, my meditation would last around fifteen minutes.

In addition to this, I found a man named Tim who taught Wu Ji healing meditation, and I made an appointment to meet with him.

Arriving at the small, austere office in our city's Chinatown, I was greeted by a tall, lanky fellow. Mildly surprised to discover Tim wasn't Asian, he smiled, promising he'd studied Taoism for years. His office smelled strange—incense and vinegar, herbs and oils— which was off-putting, without being a deal-breaker. I also chose to ignore the carpet on the floor that appeared older than I was, and as threadbare as I felt. A small shrine to Buddha sat in one corner, incense sticks and wax fruit placed reverently before it. Cute, kinda.

Wasting no time, he showed me how to sit, breathe and properly expand my lungs. Intent on teaching me techniques, he didn't seem at all interested in my story or reason for being there. I was impressed by his single-mindedness, and a little offended by his indifference.

"In times of stress," Tim explained, "we don't breathe well. Instead, we hold our breath as if we're in hiding, with short, shallow inhalations that pull all our bodily resources inside, while our high level of adrenalin keeps us going on the outside. But there's not much energy left to take in a good full breath, over and over. We must be reminded to do it."

He gave me homework, encouraging me to breathe at least sixteen rounds of deep breaths, four times. These breaths were made to a count of four in, and four out. I just needed to remember: Slow down, breathe well, and the oxygen would come full force to help my body do whatever it needed to do. Tim said the first noticeable benefit would be thinking more clearly.

I loved the idea of being supported by more meditation—and

healing meditation at that—but I also sensed that this man saw me, and was dedicated to his craft. The breathing practice centered me. I absolutely inhaled the kindness that surrounded me and accepted the fact I was going to be okay, throwing off the mantle of doubt and taking in life-giving oxygen. It changed everything, at least in that moment. I was getting used to accepting the gifts now arriving, one at a time.

After our session, Tim suggested visiting the "doc" next door, a TCM specialist. I frowned. I had come to him to learn some peaceful ways to heal myself, but now he was suggesting that we step back into three-thousand-year-old-Chinese medicine. Thankfully I went with it instead of falling into my usual cycle of over-thinking, hoping it might prove to be my own miniature Chinese hospital, just twenty minutes from home.

I stared dubiously at the "door" to the man's office, which was in fact a wrinkled bed sheet.

"There's a doctor in there?"

"Yes, he's mastered all four levels of TCM," Tim said. "He actually attracts people from all over the country."

"Do I need an appointment?"

Evidently not, as Tim had already disappeared beyond the white fabric. I tentatively pushed it aside to discover a diminutive, intense Chinese man in a doctor's coat. Now I knew where the smells originated; it was so pungent I had to force myself not to cover my nose.

Teapot at the ready on a desk near the window, the doc motioned to Tim who passed me a small cup. This smell was calmingly familiar and the flavor unsweetened; green tea perhaps? The white-coated man was talking to a young woman in rapid-fire Chinese.

They laughed as Tim and I sat on a couch and waited in silence. I felt like an intruder on their conversation even though I couldn't understand a word between them. After ten minutes the Chinese woman left and Tim motioned for me to sit next to the doctor—it was my turn. Another young woman appeared and took her seat in a nearby chair. I soon discovered she was an interpreter.

I wasn't used to speaking through a third party, unsure of when to start, stop, who to look at, how much to say, or whether I should try to explain how I felt. I decided to simply stick to the facts, nervously glancing between them and certain I was making all kinds of cultural blunders as I ignored one to address the other.

When the doc finally spoke to the interpreter, his voice boomed across the room. In spite of what seemed like shouting, I could see he was extremely calm. He looked at my eyes and tongue with a small light, and felt my pulse in both hands by applying different levels of pressure. He did this several times before taking my blood pressure, which was 100 over 60. He had a small machine and turned it around so I could see the numbers.

"Doctor says you need to smile more," the interpreter said.

It wasn't the advice I had expected, but I couldn't help but agree. "Yes, I probably do." I looked around at the peeling paint, the odd charts with words and pictures I couldn't fathom. The hospital system hadn't been right for me, but was this a viable alternative? Was the secret to my survival smiling more? I didn't think so.

Sitting there, I tried to imagine my future and saw nothing except TV snow. What the hell was I doing?

"Ni shì bùshì shingbìngle."

The interpreter touched my arm, which pulled me back into the present.

"You are not that sick," said Li, the interpreter.

"Huh?"

"Doctor says you are not that sick."

"Ask him to repeat that, please," I said, in disbelief. Li spoke to the doctor who gruffly repeated his words, before looking at me and shrugging.

"It is as I said."

Immediately my shoulders broadened, and I took a deep breath. Turning from her, I looked into his eyes and he looked into mine. He said nothing, and everything, in that one dark stare.

To this day, when I conjure the memory of that moment my eyes water, my face turns red and my skin prickles. It does not matter how long ago it was, I will always remember the look that altered the direction of my life.

Like a deer caught in the headlights, I made the interpreter confirm what the doc said twice more, as I was unable to let the words completely sink in. If this guy was right, then maybe my "contuition" hadn't been so far off the mark.

I looked at the interpreter and said, "Tell him I like what he is saying."

She did, then translated his response. "You need to go home and lie in bed."

"I can't," I said, bemused at the very thought. "I have a job, a house and a disabled son I care for." Frowning in exasperation—and with a slight air of self importance—I added, "I'm very, very busy." The daily set of care giving constructs, set in place for over a decade, was not a force to be reckoned with. There was little wiggle room.

Even if the doctor didn't understand my words, he certainly comprehended my facial expressions. Before the lady could translate, he had rattled off his response, the two dark eyes daring me to challenge him.

"Doctor says you must go to bed, listen to nice music."

I went to protest, but she raised her hand, silencing me. "Now he wants to work on you."

I nodded, wondering if I would be punished for my rebellion. Was he going to stick me full of those odd little pins?

They led me to a massage table, where I was asked to lie down on my back. With slow movements, the doctor meticulously massaged my legs, spreading a very pungent oil from my feet up to my knees. Through his strong, smooth hands it was easy to imagine feeling the combined energy he gave to the thousands of bodies he had worked on over his seventy plus years. His confidence was palpable, and after several minutes I began to feel overwhelmed with the knowledge that I must indeed be in the right place, at the right time.

The interpreter-turned-assistant lowered my high-waisted pants to the groove right above my hips and tucked the hem of my shirt up into the bottom of my bra. The doc spread oil on my stomach, massaging my midsection. After a few minutes he pulled a lamp over me (I would later learn it was an infra-red TDP light) with two heated domes. The first was placed about six inches above my stomach, the other over my face. It was cool at that point, and I tried to imagine what he might be wanting to illuminate. Slowly but surely, the heat came.

It wasn't a lamp at all, but seemed like some kind of directional cooker. The oil was spread on my upper chest, neck and face. It reminded me of eucalyptus and camphor, and I closed my eyes against the fumes as I remembered a similar salve Mother used to put on my chest as a child. The past began to bleed into the present and my thoughts were running around in my head like ants at a Chinese watermelon carving festival.

Settle down, Chris.

I repeatedly soothed myself with his prognosis that I was not going to die just yet. It was a nice change from the Western practitioners who would spell out worst-case scenarios in an attempt to avoid potential litigation.

The lamps were set on timers and I was left alone for twenty minutes, basted like a turkey with just my thoughts. Unexpectedly, my cynical brain was not bursting at the seams with challenging questions, like, *how can I not be sick if I'm tired all the time? Since when does bed rest lift your blood count? What if being forced to lie prone all day stresses me out more?* Those queries would come later, but for the moment I laid beneath the searing mineral plates, enjoying the heat radiating through my body. And hey, I was due for a face peel anyway.

"Massage upper body now," said the interpreter.

My skin was tingling, a new sensation, and it made me aware of the fact that I usually felt quite cold. He turned off the lamps and started to massage my face and head, again working quietly, definitively and with great consideration. I had never had a massage like that before, and I was amazed that by pressing on certain areas it allowed me to breathe easier, and set off a chain reaction of stomach sounds so loud the interpreter had to turn away to stifle her laughter.

Had I died and gone to heaven? It was exquisite. After about thirty minutes I was told I could wipe off the oil, get dressed and be on my way. The doc would give me a bag of herbs—not drugs—to ingest over the following week, before I needed to see him again.

One week? To someone counting down their final three months of existence, this seemed rather negligent. I could be dead by then.

"Shouldn't he be seeing me every couple of days?" I asked, swallowing my initial request for a daily examination.

"No, you are not that sick," the interpreter said. "Sixty dollars please."

CHAPTER EIGHT

The Music In Me

Choice

My transformation would not happen overnight with a single "miracle massage," but it had begun. I felt as if my eyes had been opened a tiny bit to see that the sun was out. Was it okay to even acknowledge such a thing? If that were truly the case, I could fall back into the strength of my intuitive sense of peace, calm, ease. It felt right, it felt strong, it felt like this was where I was supposed to be.

"Cynthia, you will never guess what just happened."

"What?"

"I went to learn Wu Ji Healing Meditation and on the way met a TCM doctor. Are you sitting down? He said 'I'm *not that sick!*"

"Really?" She sounded dubious.

"Uh huh. My orders are to lie in bed and listen to music. God, I'm going to have to rush out and buy some CDs. Maybe some incense..."

"Don't rush out, Chris. Relax! That's the whole point, I think."

"Of course, you're right," I said. Geez, only I could make relaxing a chore.

When I spoke to Bill, he was incredibly supportive, encouraging me to do whatever was needed, even when the burden fell upon his shoulders to take up the slack.

When David was injured, neither one of us was familiar with brain injury or caring for a completely dependent adult and all that it entailed: stomach tubes, special jersey sheets and reverse Trendelenberg beds. Little by little we learned how to work together as a team, and within months we were able to read one another's needs and directions from body language alone. Together, we found a newfound affection born between us as we relied on the skills and strengths of the other. Our marriage had started out as oil and water, but now we had emulsified into a lovely vinaigrette.

I had always been amazed at Bill's strength and patience with the process. When I could no longer handle the load, he'd been there to support my not-so-normal self once more. There were times when he leaned on me, too—the burden was too much for any one person to bear. But throughout it all, he had been my rock. Again, when I needed him the most, he refused to waver.

My daughter, Melissa, was more conservative in her appraisal of my condition and its treatment. She had attended one of my visits to the blood doctor and strongly suggested that I follow his advice and undergo the Immuno Suppressive Therapy. She seemed terrified of losing me, and after all our family had gone through, her reaction made total sense. A few tears were shed before she could bring herself to accept the decision of her excruciatingly stubborn mother. Clearly, all that meditation had gone to my head.

My son had only one sentence to spell out:

"You will do just fine."

A new hope flowered in my life, a new creativity awakened. Perhaps it was time to get another type of coach, one that would help me remember how to relax and enjoy life again. That's right, I needed a Fun Coach.

Thanks to the Internet, it didn't take me long to find Bernie DeKoven, a man who'd coached thousands of people on joy over many years. I'd almost expected some guy in a funny wig and clown costume, but Bernie seemed refreshingly normal. I sent him an email explaining my situation, and soon after we spoke on the phone.

"Usually, I coach people in groups Chris, so how do you see this happening?"

"Well, maybe you can suggest ways for me to improve my humor quotient, to keep me focused on fun. It's important that I avoid that other F word."

This revelation was followed by an awkward silence.

"I mean fear," I spluttered. "I need to stay away from fear."

"Sounds great," he said, chuckling. "What do you currently do for fun?"

"Well, not much." I thought about my release sessions in the basement...did screaming count as fun? "It's hard to find time amidst resting, eating and sleeping. I also still manage my son's care, especially when the caregivers don't show up."

"Let's say none of those factors existed. What would you do for a laugh?"

"Hmm." I was utterly lost for ideas. "Dinner with friends? Going to a show?"

"Sounds like fun to me," said Bernie. "Until those are viable activities for you, let's talk about fun you've had in the past. Do you have a memory of when fun was all there was?"

Straight away I thought of a summer camp I'd attended in Three Lakes, Wisconsin when I was twelve, Minne Wonka Lodge. I told Bernie about the archery and horseback riding, swimming in a lake and carving boats from bars of soap. The images of glittering water and a golden sun flashed through my mind. Sweaty horse flanks and grubby knees. *Fun!*

"Fantastic! Let's start there," he said. "Do you remember any camp songs?"

"Of course, how could I forget them?"

"Well then Chris, we have your first assignment. Remember as many camp songs as you can, and when we talk again, you will sing at least three for me," Bernie said.

I gulped. In certain moments, life can seem utterly ridiculous. Singing childhood camp songs to a strange man five hundred miles away had to be up there.

"Sounds great," I said.

That afternoon I reminisced about the time the camp cook had prepared liver, but put each serving in foil so that we didn't know what we were having until we all sat down and opened them up. The sounds of gagging followed by a wet, slimy food-fight came back to me in all its vivid detail. I can't stomach liver to this day.

From then on I would lie in bed and allow my mind to float back to that place, a time of youth and fun. Those days may have passed, but their essence had remained inside me, waiting to be conjured.

I could also draw upon my other Fun Coach. Years ago I had a dream about this short, older, not exactly good looking guy. He would show me which way to go, and he was always happy, and willing to be silly. I'd dismissed him as some grungy old man kickback from my subconscious. But I never felt worried in his presence, and I felt he cared for me.

One morning I woke from a dream where he suggested that I sit and meditate. I responded by announcing I had things to do. I could almost hear his reply. "Don't worry, this won't take long." With that suggestion, I sat down and closed my eyes. Within a few minutes I heard something in the back of the house making a hullabaloo, akin to a large man's hands clapping. What was that? I got up and walked to the back porch, its screens broken earlier that week. The other windows were made of glass. On the floor there was a huge red-tailed hawk repeatedly throwing himself up at the glass windows in an effort to get outside. I stood there with my mouth open, amazed by the sight before me. Here was a large bird desperate to escape, and about to hurt himself in the process.

Slowly I approached and dropped a dark blue bath towel over the creature. With the weight of the fabric, he was settling down. I placed my hands on either side of his body and picked him up. He did not move and although he looked huge, he only weighed about four pounds. It was a phenomenal experience, picking up such a powerful, graceful bird. I made my way out of one of the screened doors and set my charge on the deck.

Little by little I pulled back the towel, until he turned to look at me. I was close enough to see the small mound of cartilage on the top of his sharp, curved beak. We stared at each other for several seconds, before he promptly flew up into the nearest tree. After a few moments I went back inside, eyes wet with joy. I did not know what had just happened, but I had sensed that something else was going to happen, and soon.

After that experience I was struck with the desire to find out where the voices in my mind were coming from. I knew they were from outside myself.

In the morning the word Dubhan whispered through my mind. I didn't know what a Dubhan was, so I searched the Internet and found the only Dubhan who had ever lived. He was from the sixth century AD

Saint Dubhan, the builder of the first lighthouse in Ireland at Hook Head. It seemed I had found my Fun Coach on the other side! He would, in a figurative sense, light my way. I could always call on him to help me laugh through the crazy times, and enjoy the ride. Even if it was a bit bumpy.

I also found fun in keeping a journal. When I had the energy, I drew doodles in the margins, just to goof off a bit. I wasn't used to that, but my Fun Coach Bernie assured me this was a perfectly acceptable activity, and I learned it was a nice way to give my thoughts some color. These were added to the *Reflecting Pond*, a book I'd created years ago when first caring for my son. Its purpose was to remind me of the things I delighted in, and before long it was filled with inspirational images, quotes and beautiful pictures taken from all manner and sort of books, magazines and the like.

When I wasn't on my back snoozing or doing my breathing exercises, I had plenty to keep me busy as I began to heal, little by little, day by day. I would sit outside in the sun for ten minutes, taking in the rays. Occasionally I would look up to see that indeed, there were silver linings on clouds. Sometimes I walked around my small backyard, noting the few tomatoes I'd planted earlier in the year and were left to be plundered by squirrels. I even found out how to put music on my phone so that I could listen to the artists I loved, anywhere at any time. Suddenly, my days were filled with Patti LaBelle, Stevie Wonder, Moody Blues, MoTown Hits and lots of slow jazz. I've never really cared for country/western, but *I've Got Tears in My Ears* became a theme song.

How good it felt to be a sponge! There were lots of tears—warranted tears—and I was determined to release them. I feared that caring for myself might be indulgent, but it built me up, one beautiful note at a time.

Silver lining on the cloud above us.

CHAPTER NINE

Leap Of Faith

Choice

As I saw it, three issues loomed before me and each of them was formidable. The first was to decide if I really wanted to stay on the planet. After all, I had been offered the door, and the party felt like it might be over.

Secondly, if I did choose to stay I had to either abandon mainstream medicine, or embrace it. Intuitively, I sensed it was an all-or-nothing equation; it didn't seem wise to mix Eastern and Western approaches that were based on fundamentally opposing principles.

Finally, there was the issue of healing in general. If I didn't try every option that allopathic Western medicine offered, how could I face death with those paths left unexplored? East and West seemed to overlap and compete for first place, but if I didn't get things straight in my own mind, there would be no medal to compete for.

I couldn't help feeling that despite the small moment of hope and triumph I'd experienced, perhaps my time was up. In fact, I had an involuntary mantra: Am I getting better or am I getting worse? This repeated in my mind many times each day. I felt I had to face the music, so I found a quiet place, centered myself and began to converse. "If I'm supposed to die, then so be it. Go ahead Life, take me, because I'm ready whenever you are."

Just as intuitive messages had come to me at other pivotal moments in my life, the following words floated to the surface of my mind: "It is your choice; you need only decide what you want."

It was a recurring theme in meditation land: *ask and thou shalt receive.* But I was tired of fighting, and I wanted Life to make the decision for me. As much as it seemed that the external world was out of my control, Life refused to take over. It was clear I would have to manifest my own destiny, whether I liked it or not.

My choice could not be based on the fact I was needed by others. Years of inner work had taught me that if I did something purely for someone else's benefit, my initial enthusiasm would twist into resentment. I had to want it, too.

I also knew that sometimes it's good to wait, and other times you have to jump. For Indiana Jones, this moment came in a scene Steven Spielberg called "The Leap of Faith." In the film, Jones comes upon a huge abyss and it's clear there is nowhere to go but down—a long way down. But even a terrifying fear of the unknown is preferable to certain death. He eventually puts his foot out and voila! A bridge appears, the perfect solution to his problem, but one that could only be discovered through surrendering to that which he couldn't control. Jones had to believe in the outcome, even if the method made little sense at all.

Unfortunately, I couldn't work out how to jump into the abyss; it had already swallowed me whole. So I sat, staring through my window, seeing nothing at all.

Then, a flash of red.

I always think of my father when I see a cardinal fly by; he loved redbirds. A particularly vibrant one was swooping around outside.

"Daddy, I miss you. I wish you were here to hold me."

My mother, father, aunt and grandparents had all "spoken" to me from the other side, not in the cheesy way you see on television, but in a deeper sense of communion and guidance, and always when I asked for help. On this day, however, Daddy was clearly off catching a largemouth bass on some heavenly lake with Uncle Jerry.

I stared glumly into my reflection, and had a conversation with, well, myself.

"I am still here."

Instantly another simple thought emerged from the cloud hanging over me.

Well, then I'm supposed to be here. I strongly held the belief that whatever WAS, was supposed to be, in this moment.

Okay, why?

I have no idea.

But since I am here, okay, bring it on. I'm staying. Even though I have no direction, no desires, no path, no plan.

It was a silly conversation, and a modest thought by any standard. No big deal, but I could hear a breakout of celebration from my ancestors and guides on the other side. This bewildered me.

"Why celebrate my simple choice to stay?" I asked.

"You had to make the choice. We could not make it for you."

I had finally decided that living through my illness might not be so bad after all. But this only made me more anxious about questions two and three. Should I abandon mainstream medicine altogether, and if I did, wouldn't it be better to at least have exhausted my options with it first? As usual, more questions than answers were coming to mind. The Chinese doctor had been the first, and only, practitioner to reverse that flow. It was not long before I found myself once again at his office.

"Dr. Chen..." I lay on the massage table, relishing his healing touch, "why is it that when I sit down to rest my stomach cramps up? It only lasts a minute, but it happens ten times an hour throughout the day. I never had this problem before," I added, with a slight hint of accusation.

"Herbs," he said through Li, the interpreter.

"Right. And will I feel like this permanently?"

"No, this is healing pain."

"And how long will it take me to heal?"

A faint, almost imperceptible flicker of irritation crossed his face.

"Rest. Take time. Don't count clock."

I'd been badgering him for a time frame for most of our session, a date I could mark on the calendar with a big red cross. I was healing, but I was still too focused on the end point to truly appreciate this fact.

After beginning Dr. Chen's herbs, I received two more transfusions and my allergic reactions only worsened. The swelling and inability to breathe became more debilitating and had come upon me faster. The doctors and nurses ran around the room as if my life was under threat. It was.

Whenever I thought about the doctor's plans for ports and restarting my immune system, I cringed. I was ordered into a chair for an hour or two at a time, pumped with blood and drugs and then ordered out the door. No one there ever told me to go to bed and just rest. To me, the other patients in the blood room looked, well, hopeless. I didn't feel a kinship with them, nor did I consider myself hopeless, and found it very difficult to assimilate. In many ways my leap of faith was not so much a soaring jump into the unknown, but the only option that wasn't unbearably depressing.

One month after I started working with Dr. QiJun Chen, I went out to my garden and settled into a large beach chair. From my pocket I retrieved my mobile phone, and called the office of the blood doctor at the hospital.

"Hi, this is Chris Collins. I'm a patient there. I would like to talk to the administrative manager, please."

"Yes, Mrs. Collins? Is everything alright?"

I explained to the woman that I no longer required the services of the good doctor and that I had found other options I preferred not to go into (herbs and massage) and that I wished them all the best.

And just like that, it was over. We were done and I was free.

As the sun beamed down upon my face I wept in gratitude, joy, relief and yes, a healthy dose of fear. But mostly, I felt strong. I had just dismissed the person who I had considered most knowledgeable when it came to the central crisis of my life. I had taken the gatekeeper's key and tossed it in the sea. Who the bloody hell did I think I was?

It was a dichotomy. It made no sense, and yet it made all the sense in the world. I could choose to stay on this planet, to walk away from the beaten path, and to accept the fact I might actually be healing. Or I could give my body away to those I no longer trusted.

My decision had been made.

Another of my guides from the other side came to comfort me, hold me and give me what only mothers can give. Unconditional love. Mary, mother of Jesus, was a guide I counted on for this type of help. She did nothing, ever, other than accept me. With my choices, my body, my sorrows, she had been there for me since I was a young Catholic girl going to mass at every opportunity. We had a lovely connection and she always reminded me what Pure Love was all about. I was held in peace as the tears made their way down my cheeks.

CHAPTER TEN

The Healing Is Happening

Shift

I'd accepted the invitation, and it was time to show up.

My primary job now was to do exactly as the Traditional Chinese Medicine doctor suggested. It was summer and the days were warm, and I lounged in bed for hours at a time. *It's not laziness, but therapy!* I would remind myself, sipping my green tea as Bill rushed around getting ready for work.

In truth, it look a long time for me to be able to lie down and overcome the initial rush of thoughts that invaded the quiet. There would always be errands to run, problems to solve and people to help. It took a lot of practice to reach the point where my shoulders sunk into the mattress, and I finally relaxed. When this happened, I understood that I had been suffering from extreme fatigue. No, I had not invented an elaborate blood disease as the perfect excuse for a vacation, at least consciously. While my family instantly understood I needed rest, it took some time for me to stop questioning myself.

Mornings involved getting up, shuffling around the kitchen in my slippers as I snacked on whatever I felt like, then the slow, ambling return to bed. I would get up again at lunch, eat once more, and again lie down. I slept through the majority of July and August, and when I wasn't obviously tired I listened to music and took light naps.

Despite the hours I'd dedicated to horizontal living, the vertical parts of the day left me feeling utterly exhausted. It seemed ridiculous to be tired after a two-hour nap, but the fatigue was immense. Clearly, I'd opened the floodgates and my body was only too happy to tell me how it really felt.

Feeling beyond exhaustion and crouched with fear for many days I went to bed trembling and woke up in a state of anxiety as well. My original diagnosis and slow countdown to D Day hung over me, but I tackled each day of uncertainty as I had the one before it. Wake, eat, sleep and repeat.

Of course, with my new lifestyle came certain changes. My daughter lived across town and was nursing a new baby. Bill had to be at work and David still needed to have someone with him—usually a caregiver. If the house needed something, I was the only available family member to take care of it. But I could no longer simply hop in the car to pick up groceries. First I had to sit down for ten minutes and strategize. It was important to ensure that I didn't overdo it, and expend the energy required to make it home again.

Upon reaching the store and finding a parking space, I sat in the driver's seat and gazed at the glass doors, a small marathon away. I was already exhausted, and I hadn't even made it past the baked goods. How on earth was I going to survive the walk past the canned vegetable aisle? Glancing to the side of the entrance, I slowly headed for the shopping carts and noticed a series of electric ones under a sign that said "disabled." I almost shuffled past without thinking, and then stopped. I couldn't be one of those healthy-looking people that walk into a store and sit in carts meant for people in wheelchairs. Could I?

Turns out I could.

They don't go fast, but they do get around. After ninety days of Dr. Chen's care I didn't feel "floaty" any longer, and my thoughts weren't running hither and thither. In fact, I guided my cart around the corners with considerable grace. It was Fun; Bernie would have been proud. No one even tried to ride on the back! However, the other F word, fear, was never too far away.

A month earlier, I connected with a guide on the other side named Bruno Groening. He was very busy in the 1940's doing healing work in Germany and other areas. He would heal thousands at a time. There is a whole organization of "Friends of Bruno" that share the stories of the people he healed, and those today who recover after only holding his picture.

He always said to the crowds, "Give me all of your negative thoughts, send them to me, and no longer think these things." When I came to a meeting and heard his story, tears came, for no good reason; I felt he could help me. One night before bed I asked if he would be a guide for me and he agreed. I call him my "trash man" because he always takes out anything and everything I no longer need. Fears, worries, negative emotions, anger, extra frustrations...he takes them all. I love Bruno. That doesn't mean I am without fears or frustrations, I wish! When I recognize them however, I can hand them over. It is a wonderful feeling, and every day I let go of the negative thoughts that hover, leaving me lighter each time.

After four months of Chinese treatment, a new symptom appeared: wakefulness. I didn't seem to need as much sleep! In a separate revelation, my six-month D-Day deadline had passed, and I hadn't even noticed. Aha! Was I really getting better?

Often, Dr. Chen would discern my symptoms before I had a chance to disclose them, and my confidence in him grew with every session. He was on target, and I trusted that he knew how to solve my illness.

One anomaly I experienced was Dr. Chen's instruction to accept pain as a part of healing, rather than a sign of illness. Easy to say, but harder to practice when you've convinced yourself that you're standing under a Damoclean sword. This led me to a technique I call CrazyThink. I would suffer a pain or difficulty of some sort—let's say multiple trips to the bathroom in a short time—and the following dialogue would launch in my head: "Oh, no! Nothing is better. I'm still sick, and now there's something else. Probably cervical-damn-cancer based on my luck, and don't forget genetics! This is HORRIBLE. What will I do if I don't get better? Why delay the inevitable? We all die one day, right?"

Then some other thought would fight through all those crazy ones, often a semi-logical perspective. "Didn't Dr. Chen say you were getting better, and that you weren't that sick to begin with? And don't you feel better, too? Lose the fear, Chris, and *feel the real.* Yes that's it, *feel the real!*"

Each time these small panic cycles occurred, I noted they were shorter and less intense than the ones preceding them. Pain in any form isn't fun, but it doesn't always indicate that something is wrong. Often, it's a symptom of something that *was* wrong, and now getting better. Simple concept, hard to remember. Without having to recall, the mantra kept playing. Am I getting better or am I getting worse? I so wanted to change that mantra.

If I had only remembered one of my few rules about getting "wicked" feelings. You know, when people talk of being "told" intuitively when something "bad" is going to happen? Like not getting on a plane because something doesn't feel right? Well, I made the rule that I would never listen to those negative intuitive "hits". If I opened my sensitive self up to those types of "communications", I might have those thoughts and feelings *all the time.* That would keep me in a constant state of SCARE. I'm like Kevin James who said, "I discovered I scream the same way whether I'm about to be devoured by a Great White or if a piece of seaweed touches my foot."

So, I said to Life, "Tell me what I need to know, when I need to know it, and if it has to do with SCARE, I will ignore it, so don't even give me those hints. If I'm not supposed to get on that plane, I'm sure you will find another way." This is important for many reasons, and perhaps this story will explain.

Two days before my husband and I were to get on a plane to head for our first trip to Ireland, a volcano in Iceland erupted and no planes could go in that direction for weeks. This happened days before my diagnosis was revealed. I could not have made that trip physically, but I didn't know it at the time. I would have ended up in a hospital in some other country. Interesting, eh? No, I'm not saying that Life made the volcano erupt right then just for me. No, that would be silly.

Even so, I was not immune to Fear.

While in a store one day going through the checkout, I noticed a lady staring at the bruises running up my arms, no doubt thinking me an abuse victim or sado-masochist. Everyone weathers minor bumps on their hands, forearms and legs, as part of a daily active life, so I just hadn't noticed it. Now that I was marked each and every time, I'd become a human ink blotter.

Later that day I examined my body — a semi detached appraisal of the new bruises that each day delivered. I couldn't see my back too clearly in the mirror, but I grew convinced a new bloom of them was just out of sight. This was not a good sign. Bruises on my extremities were an inevitable side effect of household chores, but how had I sustained bruises on my *back*? It meant large blood areas coming right through my skin, the spots probably bigger than those previously mottling my feet. I called the interpreter and told her I had to see Dr. Chen right away.

When I arrived, he frowned at my frazzled appearance, and calmly gestured for me to sit down.

I ignored the invitation, hiking my shirt up in the middle of the reception room. "Look at my back!"

The interpreter related my words in Chinese.

She looked at my back.

He looked at my back.

They both looked at each other for a moment, he tapped on his head and pointed to a spot on his arm while he rattled off some Chinese.

"Doctor says go home and go to bed," she said.

"So there *are* bruises?" I asked.

She shook her long, black hair. "Only some moles. But you need rest." The wide, dark eyes appraised me as if to add, *without a doubt.*

Sitting in the car, I thumped my fists against the steering wheel and bawled in an overwhelming release of tension. Once that storm had passed, I found myself laughing. I had something stronger than fear, and greater than doubt. I had a doctor who understood. And every time he tapped his head and frowned, as if to say, *Chris, you're thinking too much,* I knew he was right.

And I loved him for it.

CHAPTER ELEVEN

Experimentation Is Everything

New Life

Each week the good doc repeated his massage, oil and heat treatment on my face, chest and stomach, and little by little it began to feel normal, even natural.

I showed him any new bruises and he made careful note of each one, writing in beautiful Chinese script in my file and recording the herb capsules he prescribed. I would question the content of the capsules and he would inevitably answer, "You don't want to know." I was sure one of the boxes had been labeled something like "*elk horn," an*d prayed that somewhere out there existed a plant with that name.

Through squinting eyes I watched as he worked, and tried to absorb his calming energy. There were times when the belly pain was almost constant, but never severe, and when I complained Dr. Chen would nod. When the interpreter wasn't present we "spoke" to each other via hands and expressions; language was rarely a barrier to our understanding.

Still, we disagreed on a few items. He didn't think I needed acupuncture, and that made me feel uncomfortable as I'd heard wonderful things about it. With a pang of guilt I decided to visit some other Chinese doctors and see what they had to say. This led to three "second opinions" and I went on to have sessions with two. Both performed acupuncture and left bruises on my skin, with neither thinking that was any big deal.

One time after an acupuncture session, I was getting dressed as I noted a large lump on my arm. It was half of the size of a golf ball and rather painful, so I returned to the doctor to ask her about it.

"Oh," she said, "it is just a blood formation." She promptly wrapped her palm around my flesh and pressed the bulge back into place. This took three minutes, but those three minutes were excruciating. Instead of crying, I found myself bent over and laughing, unable to understand what she was doing, and feeling that I might become vomitus with the agony of it. She held tight, despite my gyrations. It worked though, the blood went back in, and after asking many "professionals" how this was possible, I've yet to receive an explanation!

After that, whenever I bonked myself and knew a bruise was coming I would apply steady pressure to the area. As a result, my bruises tended to be smaller in size and faster to heal. The doctor also performed moxibustion, a traditional alternative to Dr. Chen's lamps. Heat was applied to my body by burning moxi (an herb) in glass globes for a second, and the resulting suction of the cup then attached the vessel to my back, supposedly pulling toxins from my system. It was entertaining, to say the least, though it did mean returning home smelling like I'd just spent hours in a murky nightclub.

When I interviewed each of the other doctors and stated my case, all three were quick to say "No problem!" They believed they could solve my blood issues in three to eight months. I'm a broad-brush type of gal, and I was up against a terminal diagnosis. I couldn't stop until I felt that I'd entertained all options, like a kid in a carnival game battering groundhogs back into their holes, only to have others constantly pop up. Time and time again, I needed to learn and relearn my lessons, and move through the different thresholds of understanding, until it finally dawned on me I should just stick with Dr. Chen.

He didn't make any promises, but gave me information that seemed shocking at first, only to prove absolutely accurate.

"Are you working on my blood?" I asked one day.

"No."

I swallowed my gasp. "What *are* you fixing then?"

Like a ninja sensei exasperated with but understanding his petulant student, he paused his work, smiled and said, "Digestion. Good job, and blood fix itself." This was the first time I heard that my digestion was the problem, not the blood. It did not sink in.

Another question popped to mind.

"Okay. Why is it that I can be sleeping soundly and all of a sudden my jaw clamps together? Sometimes I bite my tongue and it takes weeks for the sore to go away."

"Hungry," he answered.

"What?"

"Body want food, even in sleep," he replied through the translator.

This immediately struck a chord. Since birth, lactose intolerance had meant that the slightest dairy indulgence left me cramping and hovering near a bathroom for up to three hours at a time. Gluten caused an equally extreme reaction by middle age, and sugar now sent me into horrible mood swings. After all, sugar is nothing but food porn. Mood swings are just the beginning of the slippery slope.

By avoiding these bad guys, dairy, gluten and sugar, I'd already noticed my stomach (and moods) had settled. For years I had taken after my mother, sporting a nice little bulge. I thought that distended tummies were just "the way we were built." Apparently however, remaining permanently in the second trimester was not normal at all. The puzzle pieces were coalescing to reveal that my illness was all about nutrition.

I didn't know then that forty percent of cancer patients die of malnutrition. It's understandable that in their final weeks they suffer a severe decrease in appetite, but I think the nutritional deficiency actually starts much, much earlier. My bloating was a sign of inflammation, a condition that made it near impossible to absorb the nutrients I needed.

Over the first year, Dr. Chen set diet boundaries for me, and I added my own. The answer was clear: food was the largest and most consistent factor in my health. I had been tweaking my diet for months, but I hadn't been monitoring what happened to my body in the hours after. Unfortunately, the treats I loved tended to be on the banned list:

- Gluten: wheat, barley, rye, oats (yes oats!)
- Fried foods
- Barbequed foods
- Spicy foods
- Chips, or anything fried
- Alcohol
- Soda
- Very hot and very cold foods
- Sugar, including most fruit

If the Banned List read like a great summer party menu, the Approved List was more like something from the Amish gathering in the country:

- Organic meats, fish and veggies
- Berries (occasionally)
- Wild edibles: dandelion, lambs quarters, chicory, plantain leaves, etc.
- Fermented or cultured foods
- Soup or stew cooked with fish, chicken or beef bones for several hours.
- Green juice of celery, cucumber, cilantro, carrot and wild edibles

Food is the fuel that feeds every single cell in our body, and that was the foundation I needed to work from. I did a fair amount of research, but couldn't find anyone who had "healed" from my rare blood condition without Western Medical help. The population was just too small. Most of the communities centered around cancer. There were those who were recovering, from any stage you can imagine, focused on using certain foods as their primary healing modality. *Hmm*, I thought and as usual, I went through many experiments and experiences. Like many with cancer, I had chronic "gut" issues. But this is where things got interesting.

What I found on the websites of those folks who had revived from cancer using natural therapies was there were many more than I had anticipated. Some were famous like Chris Wark, Suzanne Somers, and Norman Cousins. Some were not so famous and were not easy to locate. They were just average people, like me, finding their way, and then going back to work. In fact, the more I spoke about this to others, the more I heard that an uncle, grandparent, or sibling had found their way to healing by making major changes in their food choices, belief systems, and their choice to eliminate all of the stressors from their lives. Indeed, it seemed that in all families there was at least one person who would not play the "medical game" and went on to live a full life. This discovery made a big difference in my own approach and opened the door to my healing.

My new job was to absorb nutrients that would help my body deal with toxicity and alleviate the biggest issue of all: inflammation, or in layman's terms, blood cells fighting each other. Inflammation is caused by eating things that set the whole digestive system aflame when it becomes unable to digest things that have very little nutritional value.

For me, store-bought dairy, sugar and gluten caused havoc in my system. I couldn't imagine that taking these things out of my internal picture would help much, it seemed way too simple! But then meditation was simple, and the most powerful tool I had ever used in my life. I had to try. I stopped eating those three things and watched for my body's reaction. This was a great beginning. My stomach cramping lessened by fifty percent and so did the diarrhea! As soon as I started paying attention, the truth came into sharp focus. Food was both my weakness and strength, as my body had been trying to communicate for decades.

Another visit to the doctor brought more rules and requests.

"You need chicken," said Dr. Chen.

"Okay..."

"Black chicken."

"What's a black chicken?" Did he mean feathers, or flesh? The feathers sounded like some kind of superstitious voodoo, and black flesh was off-putting to say the least. The image of a charred, coal-eyed devil chicken sprang to mind.

"Go to Chinese food store. Buy black chicken," he continued.

In the store, I discovered black chickens were a real thing and not some figment of my doctor's crazy imagination. The skin was black, the meat a dark grey, and the tiny body came with its head and feet still attached. I felt like I'd picked up a dead pigeon from the road for dinner. Pushing my revulsion aside, I took it home and asked Bill to cut off the head and feet, and threw the carcass into a pot with a sizeable bag of herbs the doctor had prescribed. It was to cook for at least two hours, and I slowly added other vegetables to go with it. Eventually I removed the chicken, separated out the bones and put the slivers of meat back into the stew. I'm not going to lie; it didn't taste great, but it didn't matter. The Chinese had been using these "Silkie" chickens in healing soups for thousands of years, and I could see, or rather feel, why.

The next week Dr. Chen asked me to explain the process I used to cook the chicken, and was surprised to hear I'd thrown the bones away.

"Grind bones, Chris! Eat all."

I looked at him as if he'd suggested wearing the chicken as a hat. "I can't eat ground bones!" Somehow though, I knew I would find a way.

Flexibility was a cornerstone of my healing, and I had to be ready for more change. When I got home I repeated the process and waited for the stew to cool slightly. After ten minutes I put it in the blender and created an odd, gritty version of baby mash. Down the hatch it went, one cup at a time.

But even those doctor's orders were more bearable than the ones to come.

"Hot bath not allowed," said Dr. Chen.

"No!" I argued. "According to my Ayurvedic chart, I'm a Vata and warm water is balancing." Also, I really liked soaking in the tub, but that sounded a lot less impressive.

He frowned, probably thinking it a sacrilege to bring up ancient Indian treatment in his traditional Chinese clinic. "Everything medium," he said, hovering his hand at chest height. "No hot, no cold. Medium."

In Traditional Chinese Medicine, hot and cold are important matters. They represent imbalance, and it is believed that the body and all things entering it should avoid extremes. This is so the body's resources aren't used up in stabilizing the system.

"Also, no more cold," his hand now made a sharp, chopping motion. "Ever. Wear many clothes, nothing bare."

"What if I start to sweat?"

He rolled his eyes. "Take some off." He was the King of Common Sense. I was just beginning to see how all of this fit into health. It was so ridiculously simple, and doable; how was it that in my fifty plus years of life none of these things had dawned on me?

In many ways, Dr. Chen had given me permission to take care of myself, even more than I already had been. From that point on it didn't matter what the weather was, I planned ahead. It was still summer, but now I had extra pants and tops in the car, socks and shoes on standby. I would not get cold, nor stay hot. Evidently, keeping my extremities warm was taxing to my system, especially when low on blood. Even before my diagnosis I had felt consistently chilly, and I knew this had to be related to my condition.

I'd decided that Dr. Chen was the best Traditional Chinese Medicine doctor for me, but the small voice inside myself that was always seeking answers refused to be quiet. Off I went in search of chiropractors and alternative medicine MD's, even travelling to Connecticut to meet one who was well known for his effective therapies. He recommended a regime of about thirty supplements, but I knew I needed Dr. Chen to okay anything that went in my mouth. With some of the supplements being chemical, rather than herbal, I highly doubted my chances of securing his approval.

It took a total six months before I finally decided that Dr. Chen was the only one for me. From that point on, I saw him exclusively.

While my explorations led me to a new confidence in my doctor, they hadn't quieted the doubt entirely. I still asked myself if I was healing or dying, on an almost daily basis. Strictly adhering to the plan, I had expected to return to normal—or my version of normal—in six months. Sure, it had taken years for my body to degrade to the point it had, but I'd been working with Dr. Chen for nine months by this point, long enough to make a baby!

Impatient, I wondered how many more months it might take.

Beets, sunchokes, parsnips ready for the crockpot.

CHAPTER TWELVE

"Help" (In English)

Clarity

I had walked away from mainstream medicine to Traditional Chinese Medicine and could not deny the treatments' immensely beneficial effects. My body was more responsive, I could walk for longer periods and think more clearly. Nine months in, I was able to browse three stores before having to haul myself home again, and there were smaller—but equally gratifying—changes, too. My nails were harder, and the big lumps in my breasts that resulted from breastfeeding had disappeared after thirty-five long years. I felt fantastic, with my jiggling chest and pep in my step. I wasn't fully recovered, but I was closer than I had been in a long time.

True to character, when all was going swimmingly well my dissatisfaction kicked in. After a year of treatment I bounced into Dr. Chen's clinic with a new idea.

"Dr. Chen, I think I know how we can make my healing happen even faster!"

He stared at me, silent while the interpreter conveyed my words.

"I wrote to this Chinese hospital, in China! I asked them if they would talk to you about my case." I grimaced at his stony expression, my exuberance deflating like an old balloon. "I thought that maybe you could work with them. Two heads are better than one, right?"

As the stare turned into an outright glare, I rushed on. "You can use my phone! I have international calling so there's no cost."

The interpreter paused, as if reluctant to convey the message, and finally she spilled the words in an embarrassed kind of whisper.

"I will not call hospital," he said via the interpreter. "I was director of such hospital in the past. They learn from me."

"But..."

"No."

The last word was delivered directly, in English, with a stare that could turn the bravest heart to marble.

I sat in silent disappointment, eyes blinking, until the interpreter ushered me into the treatment room. But I did not want a treatment; I wanted to argue my case. I was the client, after all, and he should at least hear me out!

I lay on the massage table while he worked on me, quietly weeping with frustration and, yes, I admit it, self pity.

There was a low rumbling in Chinese and the interpreter said, "Doctor wants to know what you have been eating?"

He always wanted to know what I had been eating, and he always wanted me to eat more, more, MORE!

"Meat and vegetables," I muttered, sick of talking about food.

"You need congee," said Dr. Chen.

"Fine."

I was surprised that he brought a small bowl from the back of his office containing a slow-cooked broth of disintegrated white rice and tiny flecks of chicken, carrot and onion. I sat up on the massage table, letting my belly hang over the edge of my pants and my legs dangle off the table. It tasted of the old world, like beans and ham with cornbread, or soft-boiled eggs from my grandmother's kitchen. I gulped it down and quickly forgot my recent, tearful indignation. It was heart warming food from another time.

At home, I searched for congee recipes online, and I stumbled upon something else entirely. It sent a prickle of excitement up my spine, followed by an immediate sense of guilt. But for all my flip-flopping, I couldn't ignore the hairs that stood upon the goose-bumps on my arms. As is often the case, one closed door here meant another open door over there.

Gabriel Forzano, DOM. He was a doctor of Chinese medicine who lived in Florida and had cured himself of a rare blood disorder. I trembled as I read his story, amazed that I had found someone so knowledgeable in treatment, who had experienced something so similar. Without thinking, I called the number listed and left a message. Within a day he called back.

"You know, Chris, when I was sick I'd wake up with a blood soaked pillow. They gave me a year," said Dr. Forzano.

"With no possible hope of recovery?" I asked.

"Yup, that was the story and I was determined not to accept it."

"What about blood numbers? The last time I got mine I was depressed for about three months."

"I ignored them," he replied.

"Really?"

"Why do it? The most accurate test is to register how you are feeling," he said.

"And you can just trust that?"

"Of course. If you can't trust that, what can you trust?"

It took everything I had not to break down and sob. I'd been doing so well, but the relief of talking to someone who'd walked the same path and spoke the same language was overwhelming. The fact that I found him so effortlessly affirmed that Life was holding and supporting me, if I would only have faith in it. Gabriel and I began to speak on the phone whenever I needed to bounce questions off someone, and he was very supportive of the path I was already on. We were getting results. He also had new suggestions, too.

"You need raw milk," Gabriel said.

"Oh, that's not possible. I'm lactose intolerant," I explained.

"That's why you need to drink it raw. The majority of people who are lactose intolerant can drink raw milk, because when it isn't heated it contains lactase, and that allows you to process the lactose."

"Unheated? What does the FDA have to say about that?"

"I don't put much faith in the FDA," he answered. "Do you?"

"Not really."

"Well, then do your own research and make a decision."

I took time to review the literature and found there was a small risk in consuming unpasteurized milk, but a far larger one associated with consuming the store-bought, pus ridden stuff. I researched in depth and found that the immense antibiotics given to commercial milk cows automatically generate white blood cells, when none are needed. Along with bovine growth hormones, store-bought milk, butter and cheese was not an option for me.

Within the day I'd found a farmer bringing in milk (in our state it is legal to buy from a farmer), and drove over to pick it up. The whole process was effortless; what I would later call NEN–No Effort Needed. Again I felt I was floating down a river of zero resistance. I was in the flow.

I downed at least eight ounces of the milk and tentatively waited for the three hours of cramping and diarrhea that would surely follow. I did not feel a twinge of discomfort. In the first eight hours I felt an increase in strength I had not had for some time. I must have swigged another three cups that day.

It came in a gallon glass jar, the top third a denser cream. "Shake it up, drink as much as you want," said Dr. Forzano. I did, and within a week my increased strength was definite. It all made sense. When I was young I loved the stuff, downing as much as Mother would let me. Being lactose intolerant, however, it tended to go right through my system. I wanted the milk, my body was craving it, but no matter how much I drank the nutrients were unable to be absorbed.

I could feel Dr. Forzano's smile through the telephone. "You need nutrients Chris, because for many years now you've been getting too little. The act of eating sugar most of your life has drained your body of a lot of minerals." He paused, as if considering his next words carefully. "I'd take a guess that you've exploited your condition at times too."

"Exploited? What, like for sympathy?" I asked, wondering where he could get such an idea. It was hardly a tear-jerking condition.

"No, to lose weight. You would drink some milk and your last binge session of desserts passed right through. Again, you depleted yourself."

I looked at the phone in shock, wondering if the man was a mind reader. It was painful to admit, but it was true. Whenever I had wanted to lose weight in the past—and surrendered to my cravings for something sweet and rich—I would sneak off and drink a glass of milk to flush it out. Like some weird form of reverse-bulimia, it meant a three hour jaunt near the bathroom, but at least I didn't have to worry about the calories. The problem was, as I got older it took me longer to recover from these sessions, and I often had to lie down for an hour afterwards. Again, my body was talking to me, but I refused to listen.

Now I was listening, in stunned silence, as the doctor-turned-medium continued. "Then of course the other system depleter: bread. Which is our go-to option when we don't have time to cook. We know that gluten is not good for the human body, and it inflames many of us in an allergic-like reaction. After causing rash, diarrhea and a swollen belly, it exits the body having given us nothing of value." I slumped in my seat, struck with disappointment by how I had treated myself over the years. "All this time you've been hungry, Chris. Starving, in fact."

Since 1994 life had been heavy and stressful, and sugar in all its forms kept me "up." Followed by the long slide down, the "sugar valley" was a painful place to be. For about a day after a sugar binge I would snarl at people, and those closest to me suffered the most. Toast, frozen waffles, pasta, ramen, cereal, crackers, donuts, Twinkies, cookies and cake...all beloved, but none of them contained anything worthwhile. If I had been honest with myself, I might have recognized how lousy I felt at the time, but it had been much easier to focus on the immediate pleasure and ignore the distant pain. Now that pain caught up with me.

"The fastest way to get nutrients into your system is through raw animal fat. That is raw milk, butter and cream. You need to make up about three cups of juice, like celery, cilantro and cucumber. Put a tablespoon of cream in each and sip it through the day."

Gabriel's other suggestion was to increase my protein; raw was best. Upon hearing his words I had a sudden mental block. Protein generally means meat, but how could I eat that raw? With time, I got used to swallowing uncooked ground beef and bison, one ounce at a time and seasoned to make it seem a bit less like pet food. But as disgusting as it was, my energy shift was noticeable, and I threw myself into Dr. Forzano's other recommendations: cultured foods like kefir and kombucha, and cultured veggies like kraut. I had a lot to learn, and I would soon reach a point where I was no longer searching obscure shops for weird products, but making them myself.

It wasn't all smooth sailing; my body had suffered a lot of abuse over the years. One night I woke up screaming with a leg cramp that started at my ankle and went all the way to my hip. Poor Bill watched in shock as I took long breaths in and out, my leg stiff as a board as I hobbled around the room. I knew a cramp meant that my muscles needed more oxygen; at least that what I had learned in swimming lessons. However, the minerals in my body were depleted, and a quick search on the Internet revealed a potassium deficiency as the probable cause. I started taking a potassium tablet whenever I drank milk, and the cramps disappeared. Success! It was much easier to cope with symptoms when I had great guidance, and easy-to-understand solutions within grasp.

Little did I know, the gate to Gabriel's rose garden was closing.

We had been working together for many months, and as I rapidly expanded my knowledge, the man was pelted with questions about food, exercise, supplements, etc. Gabriel was my key to knowing what I needed, and how to get it.

One day I must have asked him about thirty questions in a row, when he finally snapped, "Chris, you must make the decisions here. I can give you information, but you have to make the choice yourself."

I felt like the rug had been pulled from under me. "But...I..."

"No buts. You can do this, and you must. Your life depends on it," he said.

"I know, but you always have the answer!"

"No, I just believe in the wisdom inside of me, for my body. You have to trust the wisdom inside yourself Chris, because each body is different. We must all seek our own answers."

When the gate was well and truly bolted shut, I wept. It had been so wonderful to lean on someone else's expertise, to make them bear the burden of my health for a little while. I didn't want to take full responsibility for my life when another person could do it for me; I'd been there, and I didn't want to go back.

I was sixteen years old when my mother passed. Alone, I had to do everything myself, including the big decisions, smaller choices and impossible predicaments falling on my shoulders. It was an incredibly painful time, but I survived, and Gabriel was right. I had to do this for myself. That day I committed to taking care of myself, in all ways, through experimentation and experience, and a process I now call CEERR (Center, Experiment, Experience, Result?, Repeat). This meant that I would use anything and everything I felt would be beneficial, and to do so, I really had to know my whole self—body, mind and spirit, because the decisions were mine. I took full responsibility for their outcomes.

It was a new beginning and one that was clear and right, at least for one person, me.

CHAPTER THIRTEEN

Letting Go

Shift

As I put the care of myself first before everything else, the time had come to look at the people surrounding me and let go of those who did not fit. It was essential that I surrounded myself with positive thinkers, the kind who would support me even when they secretly thought I was crazy. Also, I was, like many, a "giver"— a saver of people in difficult circumstances. That had to stop. This was healing time for me. I needed to keep all that "saving" energy for myself.

I knew what I was looking for; a few dear friends and family to give me pure, unadulterated love every single day. They were the mirrors that revealed who I was, and vice versa. Indulging in negativity can be very comforting, and showing constant gratitude for the simple things in life can get boring. But my friends and I believed that what we focused on would grow and expand, so by putting our attention on the little things they soon became big, and fun. Joy and happiness could be found everywhere, at any time. Together, we didn't stay in the pain of any problem for long before recognizing the gift inherent to the situation. We accepted everything from the other—even if we didn't accept it from ourselves, and we learned over and over again that we were supported, unconditionally. With all of that working together, I just kept getting stronger and stronger.

The time came when I had to let something go that was the largest, and most difficult task I could imagine.

Bill and I knew that caring for our disabled son at home was no longer sustainable. I was too involved in making sure tasks were done "correctly", from the right way to sit him in a chair to how to give him food, and David had grown heavily reliant on my company. Bill and I had no rest until David went to sleep at around 8:00 p.m. and even that didn't guarantee time to ourselves. If he called us by hitting the wall with his foot in the middle of the night, one of us would have to get up and change his clothes, or the bed linens, or find a solution to whatever it was that was bothering him. If he didn't wake us until early in the morning, we were lucky, but that only happened half the time. When he did wake up it was usually with a big grin and cheerful laugh, so any bleary-eyed, early morning frustrations were quickly forgotten. Still, it was tiring.

"You know we can't keep this up, Bill," I whispered in bed one night.

He looked crestfallen at the admission, but there was a small sense of relief, too. In many ways, caring for David was like having a baby, full time, 'round the clock and for years on end.

"I know," he said. "Having David at home with us is the best-case scenario for him, but we no longer have the energy. What options does that leave us?"

We both agreed that we could not put our son in a nursing home. To be surrounded by those nearing the end of their lives would truly compromise his happiness. However group homes were an interesting alternative. We needed caregivers who were open to learning about the way we spelled to communicate, and the endless number of tricks and methods we had established over the years to ensure he was as comfortable as possible. A tall order perhaps, but I felt that a solution was waiting out there, somewhere.

As I found new options and discussed them with Bill, our conversations would inevitably dissolve into tears; the thought of leaving our son in someone else's care was difficult to bear. Like all of life's toughest moments, it was best approached with small steps, and one day I found a house, only twenty minutes from ours, occupied by two other disabled men. I met with the caregivers who were happy to meet my extensive criteria, and they even had the facilities to bring David to us for visits. It was the perfect solution.

Before he could leave us, paperwork had to be completed, the caregivers had to undergo training, and Bill and I had to get used to the idea of no longer revolving our lives around David. The hardest part, of course, was telling David of our plans. We began the discussion one night after dinner.

"David, you know we love you, right?"

He smiled up at me, and my heart broke. Even as every maternal instinct implored me to forget the plan altogether, my survival instinct reminded me that this was not a choice. It was an absolute necessity.

"I've been sleeping a lot lately and you were right, I'm getting better." I paused, looking for the right words, but there were none. "But being sick has meant changes, and I'm starting to realize that I need to make even more. To create more time for myself to rest."

David waited.

"So..." I gulped, and glanced furtively at Bill, who clasped David's curved hand in support. "We'd like to know if you would you be open to the idea of living alone?"

I waited for the shock and confusion to appear, closely followed by something like fear and betrayal, but was astounded when my son underwent none of those reactions. Instead, he smiled.

Emboldened, I continued. "A situation has opened up where you can live with two other guys. You would have caregivers 24/7, and you would be on your own."

He frowned, slowly selecting his letters. *Would they spell for me?*

"Yes," I said. "I've spoken to them about how we care for you, and they think they can do just as well. In fact, they have a special car that can take you to therapy, the store, and here of course—we want you to come home to visit whenever you want."

He smiled, somewhat tentatively. *When will it happen?*

"We were thinking in the next two weeks. Before then we need to go shopping for the things you will need in your new home. We'll choose photos for the walls, soft linens..." He rolled his eyes as I started to run through my internal IKEA catalogue. "It will be your place."

I would like that, he said, and Bill and I breathed a simultaneous sigh of relief. Change was afoot!

We would share many more conversations on the subject as the next two weeks rolled by, but even the fear of change was not enough to overwhelm the obvious truth that Bill and I needed to start caring for ourselves, and that doing so was ultimately the best thing for David, too. I looked forward to our relationship being once more founded on friendship, rather than practicality, and as we geared up for the big move, the general air was one of excitement. Yes!

Melissa and David, our wonderful children.

CHAPTER FOURTEEN

The End Is Not Near

New Life

Three years after I began working with Dr. Chen—three and a half years after my initial diagnosis—the good doctor suggested I go and get my blood numbers tested; I hadn't done so in more than two years. Apparently, the test results were irrelevant to him; our treatment was done. Soon, I would be venturing back into life without herbs, heat lamps and massages, and he seemed to think a written bill of health might provide that little extra reassurance for me.

I felt strange about his pronouncement—he had become such a huge part of my life. In the early days, I'd been hankering for an "end point" to mark on my calendar, but now that I'd reached my goal, it felt strangely empty. I thanked him, vowing to visit in the future if for no other reason than to express my gratitude. And the blood test was unnecessary, I decided. I felt good, and my body was healed.

Six months later I changed my mind, not because my health had deteriorated. In fact, I'd never felt better. But after everything I'd been through, sheer curiosity gnawed away at me until I found myself walking through those stark white doors of the testing lab once more.

It came as no small shock to receive the call that confirmed my blood numbers were entirely normal.

It was not so much a time of celebration, but perhaps a final little bit of confirmation that my recovery wasn't all in my head. It was real. I had the data that supported exactly what I felt. A new life was mine to have, and I would celebrate it for the rest of my life.

A small sample of my favorite books.

HOW HEALING BEGINS

When I was so sick I'd almost lost hope, something came along and turned the tide. What was it? The Chinese herbs, raw milk, meditation, energy medicine or new diet? They all brought about radical change. Perhaps it was the sheer expression of faith in each solution. The Subjective Trust Factor (STF) is a powerful phenomenon; when we commit to something, no matter what it is, it empowers us with the ability to self-heal. It might be herbs for some, drugs for others, prayers, meditations or a combination of many things. Nevertheless, it is subjective, which is why it's important for each of us to learn the most about ourselves, body, mind and spirit.

Only when we know ourselves, inside and out, are we able to make decisions that work, and have the objectivity to recognize their efficiency. Instead of making a choice and constantly wonder, inner wisdom allows one to trust the path, take a breath, allow the healing, and move on. It's quite literally a matter of tuning into your intuition, making a decision, watching for how you're affected, and tuning in once more.

Each time a choice was necessary, there was a small but definite gut feeling on whether or not something was the right thing for me. I also watched for the signs. Years ago, many times I would get my little bologna sandwich, grab a handful of potato chips, turn around to get to the kitchen table and whoosh, my potato chips would fly off my plate onto the floor. Well, in those days I would just shake my head, pick them up off that floor and proceed to eat them! I never really got the "message" that they were *not good* for me. Now, however, I get the message, and nothing fried goes into this mouth. No nutrients? Then no taxing the body with something it has no use for. Done. As far as making decisions about other things, I watched for the open doors that invited me to change.

There was also spiritual help, God, Buddha, or the Universe. In any case, your spiritual path will assist you when nothing else can. Lean on it for help and knowledge and trust it almost as much as you trust yourself.

- To review, my healing puzzle pieces are and were:
- Reading about other Revivors and learning about what they did and how they did it
- Writing to them and asking questions
- Daily meditation, breath work, yoga, physical movement
- Traditional Chinese Medicine
- Raw dairy and occasionally meat
- Weekly bone broth, congee
- Fermented foods, green juice, wild edibles, vegetables, berries
- No fried food or caffeine, no sugar, no gluten
- Commitment to my own joy and healing
- Trust all is happening in perfect timing
- A focus on what is still working well, especially when things go "wrong"
- Commitment to friendship and family, but not before my own wellness
- Daily involvement in knowing my own body, mind, spirit and it's communication with me

- Attention to daily signs of guidance from Life, and acknowledging that it keeps me in the flow (read: ease)

- Realizing I was no longer alone

These may or may not be *your* puzzle pieces, however I believe that there are three keys and ten pillars that can help move anyone back to wellness. From what I have seen in my research of others who have revived, nutrition and easing of stress are two of the three most important keys to staying alive.

Stress

Kelly McDonigal proves that stress is actually helpful in her book The Upside of Stress: Why Stress Is Good for You, and How to Get Good at It. It's our Belief that stress is bad that changes everything. Once again, change your beliefs and your world changes.

We simply do not realize the amount of stress we handle on a daily, sometimes moment by moment basis, and we discount it. That means we keep on doing the same thing and asking our body, mind and spirit to handle it without any break. That is not reasonable. Often we are in the care-giving industry or we are personal caregivers, or, nightmare of nightmares, we are both. How can we turn away from someone who so deservedly needs our muscles, our brain, our open arms? It is because we have been unable to walk away from those dire requests, repeatedly, that we lose track of our own needs and then things start to happen.

The body eventually does take a break, it breaks down, and symptoms appear which demand our attention. The body must give us signs that require us to stop. We are human, and unless we have a "pointer" to the areas that need help, we might never be aware.

Many times it is specifically that "break" that begins us on a completely different path, and one that is helpful to such a degree we are amazed because of the level of benefit.

Perhaps you have had your "breaks" and were gifted by them, in so many ways, on so many levels. Stress, given that we are in the 21st century with the mantra "faster faster" replaying in our heads daily, inoculates us early with a stance of "not good enough", "must do better" and "how can I solve this problem faster than someone else?" Will we cave to these thoughts? Or shall we practice balance in our lives in order to solve the major problems of our life and the world at large? Besides if we are here simply to enjoy these 80+ years, we will do so by loving ourselves, our families and our world. Sounds good, right?

Putting this concept into play is the challenge. The balance of joyful daily living, living through moment to moment challenges and productive work makes us crazy at times wondering which side we should be on! That's okay. The problem comes when the pattern solidifies and we keep repeating it.

Here's a way to know that change is mandatory before illness appears.

If you cannot consistently sleep, if you do not consistently laugh, if you do not consistently have the time, or the ability to eat, walk, pee or yes, do Number Twos, and if you do not enjoy another's company, be it an acquaintance, friend or family member, then it is time to stop and look at your options. What options you say? The options of shifting back to a joyful life.

Oh yes, there are always more options than we can now see. Once we stop to notice them, the changes will be apparent. We can start working on and playing with one thing for one day at one time. In fact, that is the *only* way to start.

Food

Nutrition is another key simply because we have been "sold" on the fact that food is entertainment and comfort. Food is sustenance and a help to the body. There is little help in fried foods, sweet foods, and "pretty" foods. Cupcakes are pretty, lentil soup, not so much. Fresh, whole foods will *become* pretty as you see and feel their benefit. Trust me, congee is beautiful!

Greens, roots, vegetables, proteins do the job of building the body. Since those do not come in a box or a can, we must go back to our grandparents in order to understand how to cook, how to eat, and how to build with the basics. Some people just use greens and green juice to heal, at least for a time, and I support that as well. Each body is different, and depending on the year, region, season and amount of stress, the body will react in different ways. Our job is to find what is best for us and lean in on those healing tools.

Commitment to the best foods for the body is necessary, and daily recommitment is also needed in order to stay well and be strong. This is a lifelong challenge for me and one that I face every single day. Together we can laugh about it! After all, my first book was called Lemon Meringue Life...A little sweet, a little tart!

Know Yourself

And the third key? That's easy to talk about, and darned hard to do. *Trust.*

Do you know yourself enough to *trust your decisions first*? Without David's accident, and then my own experience, I would have to say definitely not. But when I look back on all the decisions I have made for all of my life, it becomes glaringly obvious. Most of the time I was on the right track. Therefore, I have confidence in my prior knowledge. Intuition is just a channel to FEEL what is the next best step, how to make a decision, clearly look at what is truly happening, question ourselves internally, and make more decisions based on our gut feelings mixed with whatever research we choose to focus on.

What if you don't have that confidence yet? What if you have never had an "intuitive sense"? It's easy to imagine that you have not have enough experience in order to lean on it and make new choices. The fact is you do have intuition, it might just not be clear to you when it happens, or how. It is more understandable to chalk it up to logic.

Getting clear on *you* can be facilitated by Plain Vanilla Meditation. Sitting in silence for 20 minutes for 21 days can absolutely turn your life around. Then your job will only be to *notice* when strange and wonderful occurrences happen, and allow the gifts to really flow. I could write for hours on meditation and what it does to the body. But only the *experience* will help you, if you choose to walk that path. It is a sure way to know yourself more, and trust yourself absolutely.

Am I willing to repeat myself for the sheer sake of making a point? Well, yeah. My interest is in your healing. Remember?

But that's not enough. Where is your interest?

Revivors attend to digestion of nutrient dense foods like their life depends on it because it does. They walk away from stress, even if it is done one tiny step at a time. They get clear on themselves, trust themselves and their choices.

If you cannot now understand who you are and what you love, if you cannot make decisions without blaming anyone else, if you cannot trust yourself explicitly with your choices, then begin to learn how to do this by meditating for at least 21 days. It will not get you "there" but it will start the process. It will clarify the calm within you and energize you to move into the spaces you need.

"Oh Chris," I can hear you say, "you are telling me that eating the right foods, walking away from the most stressful parts of my life and sitting in silence for 20 minutes a day is going to save my life? That's ridiculous. I need more than that."

My response to you would be, yes, you *will* need more than that, but doing all those things will bring you to the open doors meant *just for you.* What personal keys will you add to this mix, and how will they help you get where you want to go, to sublime health? Only you can determine that. I trust you will, and you can look at my website to find others' websites where others have found their answers. Some have found them in extreme raw food, some in Chinese medicine, some in energy work or faith healing. But they found their keys, and so will you. You will continue to expand your answers and experiences. You go for it!

One day, a few months down the road, or a few years, you will be like the many folks who, after reviving from similar scenarios, agree that just going on with life is enough; we are all filled with gratitude as we eagerly return to all things normal, but we live *differently.* Revivors are more aware, more open, and more conscious of their choices when it comes to things such as diet and maintaining a deliberate attitude about wellness.

In my case, Bill and I enjoy heaven in every step. I continue to research others who have solved their health issues via self-directed treatment, natural therapies and contuition (confidence in one's own intuition), and it's become a passion of sorts. I support people on this path because it is the road less obviously travelled (at least in the U.S.) and of course, it is incredibly rewarding. I collaborate with those who are learning about their SUM's, and do long distance healing work when asked.

I'm studying other things, too, such as how to be a good grandparent, a better wife—even after 40+ years of marriage it's a constant education—and how to fill each day with laughter, no matter what.

If you have the desire, please send me your unique story. Perhaps you're still on the path to recovery, that's wonderful! Revivors can be found everywhere walking paths less traveled, and it's a privilege for each and every one of us to help, learn from, and enjoy those we meet along the way.

Okay, you have decided to make your own way, rather than following the beaten track of mainstream medicine when faced with a terminal or chronic diagnosis. So what is it like, being a Revivor?

It's a full-time commitment to bring oneself back from the edge. With help, you can revive yourself, after you do *just one thing.*

Let Go

Before you start off on this journey of healing you might allow yourself or your Higher Power to have it's way with you. That means if you are truly to die, and yes, we all will from this wonderful planet, you are clear about the fact that it is an absolute. And you and I have absolutely no idea when it will happen. This means you are willing to prepare for the inevitable.

Do your homework, your paperwork and your soul work. Ask for forgiveness, touch base with those you want to contact, say your goodbyes, have a funeral while you are still alive if you want to. Once that is done, if you are still here, then you can do what you wish, with no constant glance over your shoulder. You will be free to truly and ultimately experience how to heal yourself.

REVIVOR: THE TEN PILLARS

1. **From me, to me.** Recovery will require all of my energy. I am no longer responsible for others in the same way I used to be. I have given myself to those around me, and now that energy will be focused on me. I give my "all" to me.

2. **What I would like.** I will search for whatever my heart desires. Money, time and assistance are no object. I am confident that the way will become apparent, once I have made my request. If something I want seems physically impossible, I will read, listen, watch, imagine and absorb all that I can, until it is clearly enough. I am ready for things to come to me in unusual ways.

3. **What's working.** Instead of noticing what's not working, I am watchful for the things that *are*, and these represent the grand majority. I know that all interactions and reactions are a part of the healing process. I seldom make decisions based on fear.

4. **Patience**. I understand that my illness has been evolving over many years, and it may be days, months or years before I free my body of it. I am patient with the process, because I am building myself back up.

5. **Help.** I find assistance easily and effortlessly, including those who support me unconditionally and will be there for me no matter what. I am not afraid to ask for help because it is one of the biggest gifts I can give to another.

6. **Trust.** I know that whatever the future holds will ultimately be the best thing for me, period. Certifications, licenses, doctoral degrees and PHDs are irrelevant except to be used as tools for my healing. I

am best qualified to know what's right for me, because my connection with myself is greater than any textbook or perceived authority.

7. **Sorry.** I give myself permission to feel sorry for myself for as often and as long as I like. As I release things, people and ideas, it is only natural that I feel sadness in saying goodbye.

8. **Heal in three.** I will not only heal my body, but strengthen myself emotionally and spiritually, as well.

9. **Willing and ready.** I will open myself to research, experiment and experience anything I need to get well again and drive my progress forward. Critical or unsupportive elements in my life need to go.

10. **Celebrate the gifts.** I am ready to feel gratitude for both pleasure and pain, and enjoy the synchronistic occurrences as they come about. I live in the utter joy of Reviving. When I am ready, I will take this joy and give it to others; completing the loop of beneficence.

WU JI HEALING MEDITATION

My journey led me to many wonderful healers and remedies, but I truly believe the following meditation exercises are the greatest gift I can offer you, reader. I send you energy as you practice, for peace, calm, healing and knowing, accepting and loving yourself, no matter what. I love you unconditionally, and many thousands, or rather millions of other beings do as well. Suffice to say, you are being held in love at all moments, and this practice is just a small way for you to channel that energy each day.

Do you want to know why I meditate?

- I get more SUM's every single day. (This is the biggie!)
- It calms, and energizes my whole being.
- I enjoy just being with myself.
- My memory improves.
- It helps me to breathe better.
- It makes me stronger from the inside.
- It makes me think more creatively and logically at the same time.
- It's one time where I can just allow me to be me, nothing else required.
- I love the feeling of being centered and connected to every thing else.
- I feel like I am connected with the Divine within myself, and outside of myself.
- It is the most exquisite thing I can do; nothing and everything at once.

Given all of that, there are others who put it much better than I. Continue your research if you must, but I would suggest to just do it, and experience whatever you are to experience.

Ready? Let's begin!

Notice when you are not feeling too tired or emotional, and take some time for yourself. Sit in a comfortable chair, feet flat on floor and back upright. If you wish, you can have paper and pen handy to write down all the errands, reminders and tasks that will inevitably pop up when you try to hush your mind. Slow down and allow those thoughts to present themselves, before recording and releasing. When they have slowed and eventually stopped, you can begin your practice.

With hands folded in lap, maintain a comfortable but upright posture. You can always improve and get more stringent in your practice as you go, but when starting it's enough to simply hold yourself in Love, and know that everything you do is right, for you, in this moment.

If you wish, you can record your own voice directing you on this journey, or have someone else do so. I find it's more poignant if you do it, however. The reason for recording is so you don't have to read instructions like the ones below, minimizing distraction. A guiding voice allows you to close your eyes, and seamlessly move through the process. I don't find music is a necessary addition and you should speak three times slower than you would normally; this takes a conscious effort.

Healing Meditation

Allow 1 minute of blank audio, then begin recording the following message:

Sit quietly with back straight, not leaning against your chair. Know that we are slowing down because there is nothing more pressing right now, than to do this practice. Take the next few moments to get centered, and imagine a cord of bright light that comes from Father Sky through the top of the head, and to Mother Earth from the sit bones. Allow those cords to connect in the heart, or the Dantian, *or both.*

<3 minutes of blank audio>

Write any flowing thoughts which need to be captured, so Life knows that you are hearing it, responding and ultimately clearing anything that needs to be cleared.

<1 minute of blank audio.>

Pause this recording if you are not yet ready to write or sit.

Let's take one breath at a time, in through the nose and out through the nose. Same amount in, as out.

Easy, one breath in, and one breath out.

<Pause>

Easy, one breath in and one breath out.

<Pause>

As any thoughts come in, allow them to go out.

As any sounds come in, allow them to proceed out.

Then, take another breath as a cleansing breath.

Do this set of four breaths a minimum of nine times. Imagine a shelf in front of you with nine spaces, and just see your breaths stack on the shelf. Get lost in the counting, if you wish. Feel it, and know you will be sitting for exactly the right amount of time. Easy.

<While recording, go through the breathing cycles and allow for

silence in the recording, or the sound of your own breath. Sit in silence for as long as you wish; I generally allow for about ten to twenty minutes in my recordings.>

When finished with the breathing, put both palms on the Dantian, *the area below the belly button and above the pubic area, and massage clockwise three times. Then, massage counterclockwise three times.*

Rub your palms together until they generate heat. Press your palms over your face, head and then the back of your neck, three times.

You are in service to Life and Life is in service to you, and so you and all others are blessed.

Bring yourself back into this space and time as slowly as you wish, by stretching fingers and hands, arms and legs, feet and toes. Easily and slowly come back into this day and allow yourself to open your eyes. Take deep breaths, same amount in as out, and when ready, go on about your day.

Plain Vanilla Meditation

This is my version of everyday meditation and can be done whenever you have a free few minutes, or want to take a while to disconnect from the outward and drop into the inward. Depending on your experience, forty-five minutes might seem like five, and you won't wish to come back "out." You also may find during your practice you no longer feel your hands, feet, or the sensation of breathing. This is what happens when yogis meditate, and why they are able to hold single poses for such long durations. Enjoy the experience and know you will come back into regular life whenever you wish.

In preparation for sitting, eliminate or evacuate whatever is necessary. Take a drink of water, but do not eat. Notice how comfortable your clothes are and arrange them accordingly, so as not to be challenged by any constrictions. If you need to sneeze, scratch or cough, allow the sensation to come, deal with it normally and then let it go. There's no need to try and hold anything back, or deny your body what it wants.

Sit on two pillows so if your legs are in the lotus pose; they will be lower than your core. You can also sit on a chair, but be sure not to lean back into it. Sit straight up from your sitting bones with feet on floor, apart and hands either open on the tops of your thighs, or together in your lap. It doesn't matter.

Use your notes to jot down the thoughts that arise when body is preparing to be still. There will be many. Some people think of this as "monkey mind" but I think of it as a data dump. Your brain is trying to let you know all the things it needs to let you know. Write them all down. You will be amazed at how much information is in there just waiting to come out! After that is done, think of an intention for this practice, for this day. Perhaps it has to do with less pain, or awareness of how to be focused, increased cash flow, or a particular state of mind.

Center yourself with an imaginary cord coming from your core, reaching down into Mother Earth and from the top of your head, reaching up to Father Sky, this cord meeting in your heart or your Dantian. *Begin to breathe, in through the nose, and out through the nose, the same amount of breath in as out. Ask the body to make clear the amount it wants, and do not go above or below this threshold. Concentrate on only one breath at a time; how does it feel when it comes in at the opening of the nose, and then when it is exiting? When other thoughts come in, allow them to go out as well.*

Take another breath.

<Pause> (These can be from 3 to 5 seconds)

Take another breath.

<Pause>

Notice how you are. In doing absolutely nothing, you are connected with absolutely everything.

Take one breath.

<Pause>

Take one breath.

<Pause>

Notice how every single cell in the body is taking in the oxygen it needs, and with that oxygen it is healing and benefitting.

From just one breath.

<Pause>

From just one breath.

<Pause>

All is well.

<Pause>

I am well.

<Pause>

I send love to everyone, including myself.

<Pause>

With each breath.

<Pause>

Relax yourself by beginning at the top of the head, and moving down, little by little, forehead, face, mouth, and then relax the tongue. Do this a minimum of three times until you can feel the tongue is spread out in the space of the mouth. Continue down the body, throat, shoulders and so on until you can feel that you have gone over all places and parts.

When you are finished, go back to the places that you feel tense or dark and relax them again. Go back to the tongue and spread it out again.

Record silence for 10 minutes while you do this.

After this is done, sit in silence and realize there is no better way to heal, to open, relax, or regenerate, than by taking another breath.

<This silence will last at least 10 minutes.>

As you are beginning to end this practice today, imagine some type of symbol that comes to you easily. It doesn't matter what it is. Notice its shape, color, size and whether it moves, or remains static.

Bring yourself back into this space and time as slowly as you wish, by stretching fingers and hands, arms and legs, feet and toes. Easily and slowly come back into this day and allow yourself to open your eyes. Take deep breaths, same amount in as out, and when ready, go on about your day.

Remember the symbol and how it brought relaxation to you, and how it can be called upon to return this sensation whenever you want it.

In order to reap the benefits, do this once every day for twenty-one days. Notice what happens each day after, and note the changes or insights in a journal. You may be amazed by what you find.

Origins Of Meditation

"Meditation is a way to make the mind more stable and clear. From this point of view, meditation is not purely a Buddhist practice; it's a practice that anyone can do. It doesn't tie in with a particular spiritual tradition. If we want to undo confusion, we're going to have to be responsible for learning what our own mind is and how it works, no matter what beliefs we hold."

-Sakyong Mipham Rinpoche

Archeologists and scientists have discovered records that prove meditation has been in existence for over four thousand years. Considering recorded history only goes back six thousand, it seems likely that meditation surpasses the start date established so far.

The first written records appear in Mesopotamia in the period of 4,000 B.C. But it wasn't until 3,000 B.C. that writing developed in the Indus Valley, where the earliest forms of meditation appear to have been practiced. The first written accounts of meditation are found in Hindu Scripture called tantras, and are five thousand years of age. Since they are as old as Methuselah, perhaps they deserve a try?

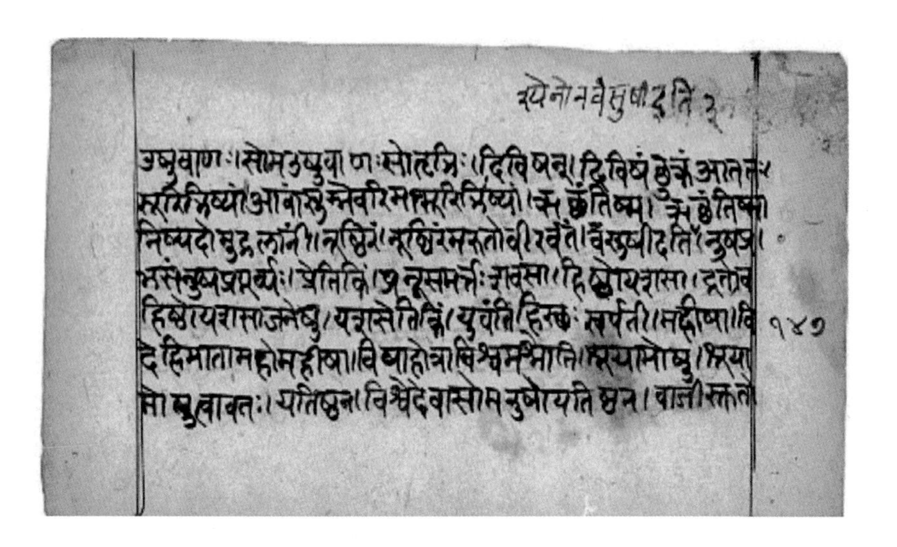

REFLECTING POND BOOK

Reflecting Pond Books are built by an individual living through a crisis, caregivers and Revivors alike. They are not for anyone but them; not their children, partner or friends.

They have tabs that are split into themes. Mine are Courage, Strength, Love, Humor, Patience and Wisdom, but really these could be anything; Prayer, Generosity, Calm, etc. Under each tab sit several sheets of hole-punched cardstock, in different colors. In each of these areas, one can put whatever they need to remind them of who they truly are. My book reminds me of Life's wonders. When you're walking through hell each and every day, it can be easy to forget them.

I started my Reflecting Pond in the early days of caring for my son at home, and I enjoyed inserting pictures and quotes from trusted role models. Some of them were by celebrities or writers, others friends and family. One was from my life coach, Sandra: "Doing things the hard way is the easiest way to procrastinate."

Piles of junk magazines appear in our mailbox each week, and there are always beautiful pictures to draw upon. Just putting tchotchkes into this book brings a smile to my face. They also give me something to review when it's two in the morning and I can't bring myself to wake another friend in the middle of the night to settle the fears churning around inside me. The book is a symbol of who I am, and what I'm made of.

Get to the office supply store and pick out five pages of five different colors of cardstock. Or ten, if you are the kind of quote addict who hordes scraps of wisdom in every drawer. Get some cardstock with tabs, or some folders. Take it to the service counter and explain you wish to make a book, with five tabs, and the five pages of cardstock in between. They should be able to spiral bind it for you.

Name four of your tabs, leaving one blank for another time, and start inserting all manner of quotes and pictures; ideas from anywhere that you simply cannot live without. These are not just nice pictures; they must be phenomenal images or ideas. If you have flat stickers or other accoutrements, all the better. Use good glue and/or tape or sticky dots, whatever works. This is a book that will build itself, and these days my Reflecting Pond book is a two-inch thick monster. If the house were to catch on fire, it's the first thing I would grab.

Example pages from my Reflecting Pond Book.

GLOSSARY

CEERR: Center yourself, **E**xperiment with opportunities you choose, **E**xperience what happens, get the **R**esult and then **R**epeat as required. This methodology can be applied to diet, meditation, energy work, physical exercise, new ideas and new therapies.

CrazyThink: It's easy to feel like you're going down the rabbit hole of illness, rather than spiraling up to wellness. But whatever is happening in your life, it's almost always better to recognize that your developments are occurring for the good, and use *hindsight* to see what has or hasn't worked for you.

IRFA: "**I**'m **R**eady **F**or **A**nything" is the Revivor's mantra. The point is to accept it all, use what you can, discard what you can't, and continue hunting for gems. First, you must be open.

NEN: No **E**ffort **N**eeded is the ability to know you are attracting exactly what you need at the right time, with very little resistance.

OTA: I am **O**pen **T**o it **A**ll. One example, at least in a nutritional sense, is a vegan being open to eating meat again, or a paleo dieter being willing to go vegan for a while. We cannot let our old belief systems rule us. We cannot close a door before we even know what is on the other side. I don't know where your nutritional "bests" are, and you don't know either until and unless you are open to it all. Calm yourself if you think you will hurl just from the thought of eating something strange. If you are going to heal from the inside out, then you will be flexible and interested in the **results**, not the dogma.

RLS: **R**ead **L**ickety **S**plit, or in other words, learn how to read fast. There are some websites to teach you. You will need to be able to read and assimilate, in order to gain information and discard what is not needed.

It really doesn't take that much to learn. This is a huge help for many reasons. You don't have to read every single word to get the information you are searching for, but you do have to notice when it is time to dig in and really capture the knowledge. Visit 7speedreading and thank me later.

SUMs: Synchronistic **U**nusual **M**oments occur in ways you could never have planned or expected. These extremely poignant gifts, ones clearly just for you, come into your life right when you need them.

After David's accident, our home became stocked with diapers, tubes, tape, condom catheters, blankets, pills, creams and cleaning items. I desperately needed what I called a "clear plastic three-level-roundy-thing" to hold it all and ensure easy access, but I had no idea where to find such an object.

Twenty-four hours later I sat at a stop light near a mall, and one of these subtle "messages" filtered through to me. Life said, "Go to the mall."

I almost responded, "I don't really *do* retail."

Despite my initial resistance, the urge remained, and with a small huff of capitulation I decided to go and simply sit in the parking lot and meditate. After twenty minutes of doing so I felt an impulse to drive around to the back of the building to the dumpsters. That small voice suggested I look around that area. I almost rolled my eyes at the heavens and said, *seriously?* But I did it, and guess what awaited me, tossed amidst the boxes and refuse? A perfectly good three-tiered Plexiglas Lazy Susan—or "clear plastic three-level-roundy-thing."

As you experience similar SUM events, journal each incident for a month and you'll see you're on the receiving end of a lot more support than you realized. At times it can feel the whole world is against you. It isn't.

STF: Subjective **T**rust **F**actor is the ability to choose—not always consciously—what is best, and be healed by that faith alone. If you believe in this phenomena and move towards a specific option that leads to great outcomes, this may be because of STF. Trust that what you are doing is leading you in the right direction. Feel it, know it, and be healed automatically. If it is not the right direction for you, it will become clear also, and you will change course. This will take you to your next step, and your next solution. But without the process, you couldn't get there.

HELPFUL LINKS

Go to my website, **Revivor.net,** for helpful links to resources and to stories of other healed people. If Revivors need to contact them, they may. My work is built for people to contact others and choose what they need based on information from others.

OTHER ENERGY STUDIES

Over the years I have continued my education of energy work with Matrix Energetics, and I've studied Pranic healing, Healing Touch, Human Universal Energy, and Reiki. I do work on myself and ask others to work on me, long distance if necessary. Seek out energy workers in your area and go to them to see what they can offer you. Often, it will be free and even if it doesn't give you what you're seeking, it can't hurt. Energy and healing surpass pills and surgery, into realms we don't yet understand. Embrace different methods with an open heart, and you'll soon discover whatever it is you need.

This cartoon is reprinted with permission.

ACKNOWLEDGEMENTS

As our friends and family can attest, there would be no book "Beyond Terminal" without my husband Bill. There would probably be no me, without my husband Bill. Thank you, Bill, for being the rock and showing me how to live in strength, no matter what. I strive daily to show you even one tenth of the love and strength you have shown me.

Secondly to my coaches, family and friends still on "this side," and my guides on the other, I couldn't have recovered and revived to write about it without your help. I bow to you in gratitude. I also thank my children, Melissa and David, for teaching me things no one else could teach me, I will kiss your feet –Wait! I will kiss the top of your heads...yes, that's better.

Finally, this book could never have been finished without the help of Dr. Gabriel Forzano, and my dear Dr. QiJun Chen. TCM does vary between practitioners, but there are many who have studied under the masters such as Dr. Chen, and they can be found at the American Chinese Medicine Association.

My warm thanks also goes to: Elise Sievers, Cate Hogan, Denis Ledoux, Ty Bollinger, Chris Wark, Sandra Hardcastle, Cynthia Correll, Vicky Bridges, Judy Ryan, Bernie De Koven, Byron Katie, Esther Hicks, Jeff May and others not named, but integral to my process. You know who you are. I will never forget who you are.

To all others in this universe, I send you Love, constant and unending, to surround you in every moment.

If you have ever been, or ever thought of being, know that you are Loved.

Chris Collins and Dr. QiJun Chen

ABOUT THE AUTHOR

Chris Collins is a woman over 60, wife for over 40, mother of two, grandmother of four and a Revivor. She has another book, Lemon Meringue Life which is about caregiving for high crisis people.

She lives in the Midwest, she enjoys napping, nature, spontaneity, synchronicity and evolution every single day. Especially when she is not watching Youtube videos of good (read:clean) comedians like Seinfeld doing stand up, Eddie Izzard and Wayne Brady. Her job is to laugh, heal, laugh some more with her funny friends and sleep. One of her happiest moments was a hug from Patti LaBelle. She would so welcome a hug from Oprah.

She wants you to know that she loves you like a rock.

Please visit Chris' website www.revivor.net for resources and share your story!

Made in the USA
Las Vegas, NV
11 October 2022